Pink Ribbon Journey
Stories From the Heart
Celebrating Women with Breast Cancer

Front cover artwork by Eileen Toth of Healing Artisan, Sewell, N.J.
Cover design, book design, and layout by Sharon Roth of GoodGrief Coaching, Sewell, N.J.
Photography by Lesha Moore, unless otherwise noted by the author

Edited by createspace

Printed by ARG Printing, Cherry Hill, N.J.

ISBN: 978-0-578-06431-4

Library of Congress Catalogue Number 2010905352

Norma E. Roth can be reached at norma@pinkribbonjourney.com

To purchase copies of this book and to learn more about Pink Ribbon Journey go to:
www.pinkribbonjourney.com

Printed in the United States of America
August 2010
First Edition

For my mother, Marlene Sosne Roth,
a pillar of strength and determination,
even in the face of adversity

Table of Contents

The author's mother, Marlene Sosne Roth, with her daughters,
(from left to right) Marsha, Debbie, Norma, and Sharon
Circa 1966

Foreword

During the past five years, many people have asked me how I got the idea to write this book. I was essentially inspired by grief. In March 2005, a year after my own breast cancer diagnosis, I learned that my former boss, Carolyn O'Donnell, had recently passed away. Although I had not been in touch with Carolyn in recent years, her death was shocking. And while Carolyn was older than me, she was by no means old enough to die from natural causes. I suspected a horrible illness took her life and found out she had died from metastatic breast cancer. Still healing from my own cancer, I was devastated by the news of Carolyn's untimely passing. She was a professor of speech and theatre at a local college and an incredibly gifted actress and storyteller. Carolyn's death hit a nerve within me, and the notion that her personal journey might never touch the hearts of others haunted and consumed my thoughts.

While I hadn't written anything of substance in many years, I started thinking about how I could write a collection of photo essays about women like Carolyn and my mother, Marlene Roth, who also died from metastatic breast cancer in 1994. The book would be a collection of inspiring stories of women with breast cancer. But, I thought to myself, the book wouldn't be complete without including the stories of the medical professionals who treat breast cancer patients. To me, they are the true unsung heroes. These doctors, nurses, and counselors devote their lives, both personal and professional, to breast cancer diagnosis, treatment, and emotional care. Without them we would not have achieved the many medical advances which are attributed to the increase in breast cancer survivors. Their stories, too, need to be shared as they are an integral part of the *Pink Ribbon Journey*. And so from sadness came inspiration, and many heart-warming stories of resilience, faith, courage, and hope.

When reading these stories, keep in mind every effort was made for complete accuracy of all factual information provided to me by the individuals you will meet in this book. Dates, times, and ages included in the stories are representative of the year the interview took place. Interview dates are listed in the Where They Are Now section of the book. Thank you for being part of the *Pink Ribbon Journey*, I hope you are inspired.

Norma E. Roth

Norma E. Roth

Maria Matos
Executive Director

Maria Matos
Breast Cancer Survivor

The first thing that catches your eye when you walk into Maria's office isn't the awards and commendations hanging on the walls, but the impressive collection of eagles adorning every corner of her workplace. There are paintings and photographs of eagles. There are statues of eagles so captivating you can't help but touch them in an attempt to capture their power and elegance. "My eagles give me strength and courage to face any challenge," Maria says in a voice that carries a strong Puerto Rican accent. This revered bird has guided Maria through all of her personal challenges, including her one with breast cancer.

Maria's journey began at her office, where she is the executive director of the Latin American Community Center, a multimillion dollar agency, quietly nestled in the Hispanic neighborhood of Wilmington, DE. The center is where she spends the majority of her day, overseeing a large staff while juggling a full schedule of meetings, fundraisers, and community outreach programs.

Tuesday morning, October 19, 2005, started off as usual for this fifty-six year-old executive. Maria reviewed her schedule, met with staff, and then took a phone call from her doctor. "I have so much to keep my mind occupied that when my doctor said there was calcification in my annual mammogram, I really didn't think much of it," Maria says, while taking a seat at the small conference table in her office. "So when I heard his words, 'You have cancer,' I was absolutely shocked," she whispers. "I mean I was numb. The words from the doctor were

unbelievable." She shakes her head, distraught, as if she is hearing them again for the first time.

Maria received the news just as a local Roman Catholic bishop arrived for a tour of the center. "I couldn't really dwell on it because the bishop was waiting downstairs in the lobby. So I just left it here on the top of my desk," she says, patting her pile of papers, "and I went downstairs and gave the bishop a tour of our building, talking with him, showing him everything we do."

"You know, some people look at the glass as half-empty, but I'm the half-full person," she smiles. "It's so much easier to be positive than negative. And the bishop, he was so calming. I felt, how ironic that he was here on the day that I was diagnosed with breast cancer. I felt as though I had an angel with me that day, in the form of the bishop, and it became much easier to deal with the shock."

The center prepared a traditional Puerto Rican luncheon for the bishop. After dining, Maria decided to tell him about her diagnosis. "I didn't want to ruin his lunch!" she jokes. "I wanted him to bless the corners and the entrances to the building. So on his way out I said to him, 'I want you to say an extra prayer for me, because this morning I was told that I have breast cancer.' Well," she says, slamming her hands down on the conference table laughing, "the bishop looked at me like, 'Oh my God, this woman is amazing!' because I went around with him all morning like nothing was wrong. But he did pray that very day

"My eagles give me strength and courage to face any challenge."

for me and I knew that he had opened that extra door and that God was going to help me through this."

A devout Christian, Maria always thinks about the presence of Jesus in her life. "I believe in Jesus Christ and I just have the light of him around me," she says, swirling her hands over her head. "But at home alone in the evening, I would cry and ask, 'Why me and why this?' But you just have to accept it," she says of her diagnosis. "What can you do? You keep going and keep moving in the process of life."

"Well, at this point, cancer claimed my schedule," Maria says, pointing over to her

desk. Caught in that whirlwind of diagnosis, doctor's appointments, and further surgical procedures, she remembers everything happening at rapid speed. "You really don't have time to think. And the doctors don't play around. I had one mission, one agenda. To stay alive! Everything else was secondary. If I was going to be six feet under, my agenda wouldn't matter, right?" she says, shrugging her shoulders.

"So I needed to take care of myself. And for the first time in my life I had to be selfish and centered on keeping myself alive," she adds. "It was difficult because I am always taking care of someone else-my parents, kids, an

3

employee, or a friend. And never, ever in my life had I been sick or in the hospital. Now I get the worst-case scenario. But this time I had to stop and say to everyone, 'I need help.' "

Maria was the first in her entire family to ever have a cancer diagnosis, and it quickly became the focus of her close-knit family. "Everyone came to an appointment, and I mean everyone," she laughs. "My parents, my kids, and my sister, Olga, they would all walk into the doctor's office, and I would just wave my hand and say, 'Oh, don't worry, pretend they're not here.' That's what it was like through my whole journey."

Based on her initial biopsy, Maria's breast surgeon thought she had in situ cancer, but the pathology found she had invasive estrogen receptor-positive and HER2neu positive breast cancer. This specific type of cancer tests positive for a protein called human epidermal growth factor receptor-2, which actually promotes cancer cells. Unfortunately, HER2 positive breast cancer tends to be more aggressive than other types of breast cancer and can be less responsive to hormone treatment.

A week after the biopsy, Maria underwent a lumpectomy. "You never know with these things," explains Maria, "only after the edges are tested in pathology does the doctor know if he removed everything." Unfortunately, the excised tumor did not have clean edges and Maria found herself having to undergo a second lumpectomy a week later. This one included the removal of two lymph nodes. "Thank goodness after this one, the edges were clean and the nodes were negative."

Maria was referred to an oncologist at the Helen Graham Cancer Center in the Wilmington Medical Center. "My doctor didn't play around, didn't mince words," she says, impressed with his forthright bedside manner during their first meeting. "My family was there with me but the doctor said straight out, 'Maria, the story is you have a very evil cancer.' He called the HER2 very evil. He told me if the cancer comes back it will kill me. He was very straight up, and I appreciated it. That kind of talk allows you to make the decisions that are going to save your life."

The doctor recommended Maria have the Oncotype DX Test, a new diagnostic test developed to assess the likelihood of recurrence for patients with Stage I and II, estrogen receptor-positive, lymph node negative breast cancer. " 'Some women like you in six months would get it back,' he explained, 'and those that didn't we considered lucky.' " It wasn't about luck, he told Maria, it was about the genes, and he advised her to have the test even though her lump was small and she was considered a low risk for recurrence. But the test came with a hefty price tag, $3,200, and Maria's insurance company would not cover the expense. Maria went ahead with the test anyway, exclaiming, "If I'm below the ground, somebody else is going to use the money, so I might as well spend it. I think my life is worth $3,200!" Sure enough, the test concluded that Maria's risk for a recurrence was very high.

Maria was prescribed an aggressive chemotherapy regimen of Adriamycin, Taxol, and Herceptin, each administered at different times. The Adriamycin, a potent

Maria, always looking on the bright side of life, relished her new look and considered her baldness a somewhat blessing in disguise. "I enjoyed the fact that I didn't have to dry my hair, curl my hair. I didn't have to spend time getting it colored. I walked around as proud as a peacock with my bald head," her eyes beam proudly. "I didn't wear a scarf. I wore a hat in the summertime because the sun was so hot, but inside I walked around bald, showing everyone this was me in the here and now!"

Baldness was something Maria could live with, but the side effects of chemotherapy left her debilitated, so badly that she was hospitalized for dehydration. "The Adriamycin attacked my stomach," she explains. "I was in a constant state of queasiness and fatigue. The Taxol attacked my bones, causing joint pain and peripheral neuropathy. For three to four days after the treatment I would have to use a cane just to walk from my bedroom to the bathroom, that's how bad the pain was," she recalls.

"I had hair loss, nausea, constant nose bleeds, low blood counts, yet I still managed to go to work. I made time for my family, my three kids, and three grandchildren. I controlled the cancer, it didn't control me," she declares, shaking her finger vigorously in front of her face. "I let the chemo knock me down for about four days and then I recuperated. I would stand up and keep going."

Six months of chemotherapy was followed by thirty-three radiation treatments which Maria describes as the absolute worst part of her entire journey. She had terrible anxiety

chemotherapy drug, stripped every single hair from Maria's body. She says she really wasn't that attached to her hair. "But I also didn't want to see it come out on my pillow," she says, patting her shiny locks. Before her first chemo treatment, Maria had her hair cut extremely short. "After my first treatment I would touch my hair lightly and see it in my hand, so I said to my son, Ruperto, 'Come shave my hair off, shave it all off.' My parents live with me and I didn't want my mom to see it in the bathroom, she'd get upset. So Ruperto came over with his clippers and shaved my head. I know it was hard for him, but we got to spend some real quality time together. He was very gentle and kind about it."

about the machine and the room, so terrible that she actually had to be treated by a psychiatrist. "I couldn't handle the room… the sound of that room," she says shaking her head. "The door was thick and when they closed me in there, I felt like I was being buried alive. And the machine would just go 'Zzzzz' and I would start shaking and trembling. The doctors and nurses were very patient, very understanding. They suggested I bring in some music CDs to help calm my

Maria realized breast cancer is not a subject widely addressed within the Latino community and made it her mission to educate Latino women about it. "The Spanish newspapers told my story and I would make sure to say, 'Yes, this can happen to you,' " she remembers. "There was a tremendous outpouring of love. I didn't know how much people loved me until I had this cancer! There were always flowers and piles of Hallmark cards and

"I had one mission, one agenda. To stay alive! Everything else was secondary."

nerves, so I brought in Julio Iglesias. Thank God for Julio. I did all my radiation treatments with Julio singing, 'Let's Dance' in my ear," Maria laughs.

A year after treatment, Maria's hair has finally grown back. She's given up coloring her hair for good and the beautiful salt-and-pepper tones frame her pretty, robust face. She still suffers from joint pain and peripheral neuropathy, both side effects from the Taxol. But her journey has left her stronger emotionally, giving her a renewed zest for life.

Maria recently traveled to Puerto Rico with one of her colleagues who also had breast cancer. "We went through the journey together," Maria says. "I am so glad I came out public with my diagnosis, because as my friend says, I may have saved her life. She was contemplating skipping her mammogram since she had missed her appointment. But once she heard about my diagnosis she went for her mammogram and was immediately told she had breast cancer."

candy here in my office! Helping my friends by sharing my own journey with them and other people helped me cope better," Maria says.

Beaming rays of the afternoon sun light up Maria's corner office while she sits in front of a bookcase where several of the eagles in her inspiring collection are perched. The sun's illumination provides a touching juxtaposition of the two images. "You know," she says in a quiet, gentle voice, "people think cancer equals death, and it really doesn't have to be like that. I am a strong person and believe that the mind is a powerful tool. Positive thinking is first and foremost for survival. My sister, Olga, and I, we're very close. She went to every single treatment with me. Do you know she still cries when we're together? And I tell her, 'Olga, you don't have to cry anymore, I'm fine.' " Like the eagles she so passionately admires, Maria spreads her wings and soars higher and higher.

Catherine W. Piccoli, MD
Woman's Breast Imager

Dr. Piccoli smiles as she enters the Women's Imaging Center waiting room at South Jersey Radiology Associates in Voorhees, NJ, her wavy caramel hair bouncing as she walks by. A quick glance at her slender, fit figure and glowing complexion, and you might mistake this top-notch radiologist for a cover girl. However she appears, one thing is certain, there is a quiet determination and self-confidence about Dr. Piccoli, named by *Medical Imaging* magazine as a "Top Woman Imager."

After graduating Harvard Medical School in 1983, Dr. Piccoli interned at Hahnemann University Hospital in Philadelphia, PA. She completed both her residency in diagnostic radiology and an Ultrasound/CT/MRI fellowship at Thomas Jefferson University Hospital, also in Philadelphia. Dr. Piccoli's journey to becoming a nationally recognized woman's imaging specialist began quite by accident.

"When I entered medical school I wanted to go into Ob/Gyn and deliver babies," she says, giggling. "I ended up doing radiology and thought it was the most fun thing in the world with all of the different gadgets and being involved in every aspect of medicine. I forgot about delivering babies. When I finished my residency I disliked mammography," she says. "I remember thinking when I finished my fellowship and took a job I would never have to read another mammogram."

In 1990, Piccoli joined the staff at Jefferson Hospital. "I loved Jefferson," she says. "All of my mentors were there and there were exciting things happening. Initially I was asked to do ultrasound, a little MRI but when I got there, they said they really needed someone in mammography," she says laughing, "and I thought, I really want to be here, so I'll do it."

From her days as a resident and fellow at Jefferson, Piccoli knew the ultrasound division inside and out and was also friendly with its director. "I got to be involved in a multi-institutional ultrasound project looking at breast lesions," she explains. "As a result we got some very nice equipment. This opened up a whole new world in breast imaging. Suddenly you could see things much better and we were out to prove that with ultrasound you could pretty much determine if a mass was benign or malignant."

With the new equipment and her ultrasound and biopsy background and training, she started doing ultrasound-guided biopsies. "Since I was part of the MRI division, and breast MRI was just beginning, I was involved in that too. So I have been doing breast MRIs since 1992—a long time, longer than a lot of radiologists. So that was the other fun thing about breast imaging that was totally new and open and fascinating," she says enthusiastically.

In 1999, Piccoli became the director of Jefferson's Breast Imaging Services, responsible for overseeing seven radiologists and a dozen or so technicians. At that time the center performed approximately 30,000

breast-imaging procedures annually. By the time Piccoli left Jefferson she was conducting about six to ten breast MRI's a day, a significant number for a breast-imaging center. Piccoli believes there are numerous reasons for using MRIs because, "More and more we're using it to stage cancers and to evaluate breasts that indicate problems on mammography and ultrasound."

South Jersey Radiology Associates (SJRA) courted Piccoli and in August 2006 she became the new director of their women's imaging center. Many in the field view her appointment as an important step to elevating

Piccoli spends the bulk of her day reading mammograms from four very large and sophisticated computer screens. The bookcases are stacked with medical journals, books, and ledgers. There are no windows in her office. On a desktop, a single lilac flower leans slightly in a paper cup, a scented reminder to the doctor that it's springtime outside.

Dr. Piccoli relaxes back in her chair and describes the important differences between a radiologist and a woman's breast imager. "A radiologist doesn't have as much insight on how biopsies are done or treatment and

"A lot of women think they are losing their breast and dying, and it doesn't have to be that way today. We try to find cancers early and treat them."

the breast cancer diagnostic services of the South Jersey region. As the Director of Women's Imaging, Piccoli is responsible for establishing an integrated women's imaging program with comprehensive services, including digital mammography, ultrasound and MRI screening, and ultrasound and MRI-guided biopsies.

Piccoli's office, a small, cramped room, is located at the end of a brightly lit hallway, beyond all of the screening rooms. The low humming sound of several computers reverberates around the office. This is where

the types of medication used," she points out. "So when people talk about a woman's imager, they mean someone who goes beyond the mammogram, recommending the correct type of biopsy and speaking with the patient and referring doctors."

Piccoli attributes her extensive knowledge and training to her years at Jefferson Hospital and working closely with the surgeons and oncologists there. "It was a very good experience and rewarding professionally. With my background I know enough to pick up the phone and tell a referring physician what I'm seeing and what the next thing to do is. I think they didn't really have a breast imager on the staff here at SJRA," she says, "but they're learning what the benefits are to having one."

Swiveling around to the computer screens, Piccoli makes a few clicks of the mouse. Instantly breast MRI pictures appear on the screens. While looking at the breast images, colored with yellow, blue, and green, it is easy even for a layperson to see how the quality of breast imaging has improved in the past fifteen years. The images are very crisp and very clear. Piccoli notes that film screening is gradually being replaced by digital mammography. "Digital mammography is better at least for some populations of women," she says, "because it sees through the breast tissue better." The future of breast screening, she offers, lies with digital tomosynthesis, which is currently available only for research purposes. Unlike mammography that compresses the breast and records pictures of the breast tissue on top of itself, tomosynthesis creates three-dimensional images of the breast using X-rays.

"The way you look at mammography now, it's like looking up at a tree trying to find the nest in the tree, which is very difficult sometimes with all of the leaves around," she says, tilting her face up towards the ceiling while lifting her hands over each other high in the air. "But when the leaves are gone, like the fatty breast tissue," she says, quickly putting her hands back down on her lap, "it's much easier to see the nest up there. With tomosynthesis we'll be able to see slices

through the breast and see the nest in a given slice. The nest won't be obscured."

Radiologists, unlike most other doctors, have few opportunities to meet their patients face to face. For Piccoli it's no different, but when she does meet them it is usually to tell them they need a biopsy. "I always look on the bright side of things and tell them that most biopsies we do are benign. I really try to alleviate any fears they might have." Piccoli encourages her patients to take it one step at a time and reminds them, "If it's a cancer, we can fix it." Piccoli doesn't tell a patient she has cancer unless she has done a biopsy on that patient. "Depending on what they have, there might be different treatment options. A lot of women think they are losing their breast and dying," she says sympathetically, "and it doesn't have to be that way today. We try to find cancers early and treat them. It can be very difficult; some patients are very teary-eyed and anxious."

Piccoli admits she is seeing a lot more of younger women with breast cancer. "Proportionately, young patients in their thirties aren't getting mammograms," she explains. "We're not finding the early cancers in these patients; they're the ones coming in with a lump. And then we ambush them and they always seem shocked. I'm shocked every time," she says, putting her hand to her chest, "and it happens every week."

"The most difficult time I ever had telling a patient she had cancer was with my own sister," she says, her voice rising and crackling. "She had her mammogram

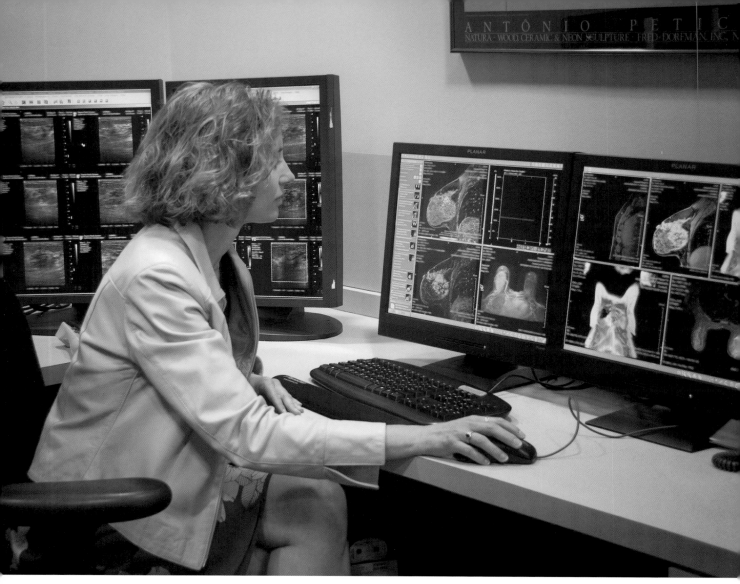

somewhere else and they recommended a follow-up mammogram because of calcifications." She blinks back the tears and steadies her voice. "About three months after she had the mammogram she brought it to me to look at. They had circled some calcifications. I thought they looked benign. But there were other, irregular calcifications. They weren't easy to see. And for one week I sat on those films and stared at them deciding whether or not I was going to put my sister through a biopsy."

In the end Dr. Piccoli performed the biopsy on her sister. "I remember I got the phone call that it was malignant just as I was about to see a patient. I had to tell this patient I thought she needed a biopsy. I happened to have a surgery fellow with me that day. I got the phone call and I just started to cry," she whispers as her eyes become teary, "and I had to go talk to this patient who was sitting there. It was so difficult to keep my mind on this patient. I was happy for the surgery fellow, who recognized that I was having a hard time and jumped right in with the patient." Piccoli's sister underwent bilateral mastectomies and is now fully recovered.

"The most difficult time I ever had telling a patient she had cancer was with my own sister... I got the phone call and I just started to cry."

Surprisingly, Piccoli says the most difficult part of her job is not telling a patient she has cancer but rather keeping up with her very hectic day-to-day schedule. "Usually patients are stacked one on top of another. I can't take forever to make a decision about what's going on," she says. "I have a schedule that I have to move through. I'll be trying to decide what I want to do about these calcifications or that mass and I'll have a line of techs behind me wanting my attention. That," she declares, "is the most stressful part of my job!"

Whether she's stressed or calm, cool, and collected, Dr. Piccoli is at the top of her game. Her stealth diagnostic abilities have earned her Top Doc honors by *Philadelphia* and *South Jersey* magazines. The most prestigious honor comes from *Medical Imaging* magazine. Each year the magazine surveys peers in Piccoli's profession in a search for the best and brightest in the field of radiology. In 2006, Piccoli was named the nation,s "Top Woman Imager" (in 2007 she made the number-six slot).

When she found out about this recognition she was shocked. "I was in total disbelief," she says, laughing. "My name was there with some very illustrious people. But I do feel as though I work hard, and I think the people I work with have respect for what I do. And it was nice, very, very nice, to be recognized for something I do well," she says modestly.

Dr. Piccoli leans against her armchair, her chin resting in her hand while a smile emerges across her face, brightening the room like the sun on a summer day.

Traci-Ann Delisser
Surviving Daughter

It's about 5:30 p.m. and Traci-Ann's workday is winding down. Her phone has finally stopped ringing. The hallways outside her office in center city Philadelphia echo with the footsteps of coworkers heading for home. It's this quiet time of day when Traci-Ann becomes melancholy; when she finds herself deep in thought remembering her mother, who died only six months ago, in November 2005, from breast cancer. The pain of Traci's loss is written all over her face. In spite of the tears slowly streaming down her face, Traci is determined to share her journey and the enduring bond between a mother and her daughter.

"Growing up in Jamaica, Mommy was the rock of our family. Daddy was there, but Mommy's the one who kept the family together," Traci says in her soft-spoken voice. "My sister, Denise, and I always came first, no matter what. Mommy was always doing community and charity work. As long as I can remember Mommy was a giver. If someone needed a ride to a doctor's office she would drive them. If someone needed help with errands, she would assist them. That was just Mommy's way. She enjoyed helping others even when she was sick with cancer."

In October 2003, Traci-Ann's mom, Elaine Delisser, felt a lump in her breast and went to her doctor, who did a breast exam and then sent her for a mammogram. The mammogram came back normal. "Meanwhile, Mommy never told anyone about this," says Traci, shaking her head in frustration. "Some time passed and she still felt the lump so she went back to her doctor who recommended a biopsy. Then Mommy telephoned me saying she had to go for a breast biopsy and she was scared."

"I was stunned this was going on," Traci says, her voice rising. "But it was typical of Mommy not to say anything. She never liked to worry me or my sister or ever have us take off work for her. Of course, I flew to Jamaica to go with her for the biopsy. Honestly, I thought it would be nothing," she says, half laughing. "But when we were at the doctor's office a few days later and he told us it was cancer, I was in absolute disbelief! I remember thinking, 'This is not what he is saying.' But in Mommy's mind she knew it was cancer. At the time, I think I was in shock more than she was."

Traci extended her stay in Jamaica and tended to her mother during her mastectomy surgery and recovery. Afterwards, Elaine began her chemotherapy regimen. "I have a cousin here in the United States who is a doctor, and she suggested Mommy come here to get her chemo treatments. But Mommy really wanted to have her chemo treatments in Jamaica," Traci explains while she stands up.

She walks over to her desk and returns to the small conference table clutching a box of Kleenex. As she sits back down, Traci pulls a tissue from the box and wipes her teary eyes. "You see, Mommy spent her entire life in Stony Hill, it's a small town outside of Kingston. All but one of Mommy's siblings had moved to America by the 1960s,"

"When I think about Mommy,
I would never doubt her love for me."

Traci explains. "Even when my sister and I moved to the States, Mommy stayed behind in Jamaica because she didn't want to leave Grandma. Grandma was about forty when she had Mommy. So when all of Grandma's other children were grown she had this little baby at home. Mommy and Grandma were extremely close, and Mommy stayed with Grandma to make sure she was alright. They lived together until Mommy died," Traci-Ann sniffles.

"Anyway," Traci drums her fingers lightly on the table, "I kept calling Mommy pleading with her to come up here for her chemo. She really resisted, had all of these excuses. She didn't want to leave Grandma. She didn't want to leave her home. But eventually I persuaded her and she stayed with our family in New Jersey while undergoing chemo treatments. I went almost every weekend to see her. She was taking Taxotere. I remember she would be in bed weak from the chemo. And to me it

14

was the worst thing ever, just seeing her in that condition." After six long months of chemo medicines which left her physically and emotionally weakened, Elaine mustered what little strength remained and made the trip back to her much-missed mother and Jamaican home.

Traci stares blankly out her office window, deep in thought of the memories. "Mommy had a lot of friends in Jamaica," she says, turning back to the table, "but only a handful knew that she had breast cancer. Most people thought she went to the States to visit her family. So when she returned to Jamaica with her hair only just starting to grow back, people would say, 'Oh Elaine you have a different hairstyle, hmmm,' " Traci-Ann says, half smiling. "But Mommy never came out and said to anyone, 'I have cancer.' And when I asked her why she didn't tell people, she said she didn't want people feeling sorry for her. I said, 'Mommy, they're not going to feel sorry for you, they're going to want to help you and support you.' " Tears swell in Traci's eyes. "Mommy had a lot of pride. It's how she was raised. She just didn't like to burden other people with her own problems."

By the fall of 2004 Elaine was not feeling well. "Every time something was wrong Mommy called me, not my sister. She just relied on me more that way. So sometime in November Mommy called me saying recent blood tests had traces of the breast cancer and that her doctor recommended radiation." After hanging up the phone with her mother, Traci-Ann made arrangements with her employer for more time off to care for her mom.

During the year, Traci-Ann made more than a half-dozen trips to Jamaica to manage and care for her ailing mother. As the months passed, Elaine's cancer continued to spread, even after radiation therapy and a second round of chemotherapy. "At some point Mommy knew she was dying. When I was with her she would say to me, 'Traci, I've had a good life. I have no problems dying.' I told her not to talk about death but she would say, 'It's happening. It's okay.' "

"People tell me there's a big void that's left by Mommy's death. I do hope she realized how much of a role she played in so many people's lives. That she made a difference to people." Traci-Ann does her best to pat the tears streaming down her face. By now the table is littered with a pile of damp tissues.

"After Mommy's funeral this guy she knew came to see us at her house. He told me he had seen Mommy a few weeks before she died and told her how he needed to pay some school fees but he didn't have the money. He said Mommy went into the house and came back out, handing him the cash he needed for his tuition. A few days later he came by to repay her the money. To him it was a loan. But Mommy told him she didn't want the money, he needed it more than she did." Traci-Ann nods her head and smiles weakly. "I can still remember Mommy saying to me since I was a little girl, 'Someday, Traci, it all comes back to you.' "

"It's been really hard since Mommy died. Sometimes I can't sleep at night. That's when I start thinking about her," Traci-Ann whispers, shuffling in her chair. "I start having all of these questions. Did Mommy

"Mommy was always doing community and charity work... She enjoyed helping others even when she was sick with cancer."

know how much I really loved her? Does she know how much I miss her? I feel the hardest part is not being able to pick up the phone and call her."

"You know, no matter where I was in the world, I always made it a point to spend Christmas with Mommy. And whenever I felt sick or something was wrong, I called Mommy. She could always sense things. Sometimes she'd say to me, 'Traci, I'm sending you a ticket so you can come home. We'll spend a few days together, just you

and me.' Mommy may not have been able to help me with every problem I had but she always made me feel better."

Traci's heartache is visible through her broken smile. "Recently," she says, "a friend said to me, 'It's hard, Traci, no-one loves you like your mother.' And you know, it's so true. When I think about Mommy, I would never doubt her love for me."

Traci takes her hand and wipes a teardrop one last time.

Robert G. Somers, MD
Breast Surgeon

Except for the lone valet attendant, it's completely desolate outside the Marion-Louise Saltzman Women's Center at Albert Einstein Medical Center in Philadelphia, PA. But inside, the waiting area of breast surgeon Dr. Robert Somers' office is bustling with activity. There is not a seat to be had among the dozen or more chairs that line up against the floor-to-ceiling windows. They're occupied with women of all ages and ethnicities, living examples that breast cancer does not discriminate. Some are here for annual check-ups or follow-up appointments, and some are here for the first time. Some of the women are relaxed, flipping through the assortment of magazines on the tables, while others appear a bit anxious, clutching the manila envelope that holds their mammogram films.

The numerous degrees and certificates hanging on the wall in Dr. Somers' office are a testament to his accomplished career. He is even named a Top Doc by *Philadelphia* magazine. Somers considers himself blessed to have spent his career at Einstein, a recognized teaching hospital. This setting has given him a unique opportunity, to not only treat thousands of patients, but to also teach hundreds of medical students and surgical residents, many of whom continue practicing in specialties all over the country and mostly in high academic settings.

Dr. Somers has a gentle demeanor, unpretentious manner, and witty sense of humor. His journey to becoming a leading breast surgeon began in a fellowship at

Memorial Sloan Kettering in New York City. In June 1966 he started practicing at Albert Einstein Medical Center. "I did thyroid cancer, vascular surgeries, kidney transplants, and radical mastectomies," he says of his early days. "I did modified mastectomies, and something called the extended radical mastectomy."

Sitting at his desk, Dr. Somers offers a brief history on the evolution of breast cancer treatment during his expansive forty-year career. "Somewhere in the 1960s someone began to realize it didn't matter if it was the biggest radical mastectomy, a modified radical mastectomy, or a radiated breast—the same number of women with breast cancer were getting cured no matter what you do to the breast," he explains, "and this for the first time proved that radiation can sterilize breast cancer cells in a breast. And then in the seventies we started to see some results with lumpectomies getting published in medical journals, so in the eighties we started doing them. The next thing you know some big operations are getting smaller."

"I am very big into women's choices, and I respect how women are proud of their bodies," he comments. In 1980, Dr. Somers performed his first lumpectomy on a patient after hearing about the results of some lumpectomy studies. "I told my patient I could do a lumpectomy and get the same results. She agreed to the surgery. She lives in Maryland now but still comes up for her annual check-up. It'll be twenty-six years this June from her surgery," he reflects.

In the early 1980s, Dr. Somers came up with the idea to create a Breast Cancer Multidisciplinary Program at the hospital, the first of its kind in the region. The program would provide comprehensive care including radiologists, breast surgeons, and oncologists. With his leadership and hospital support the program started in 1982. Dr. Somers has served as the director since its inception and also as the chair of the Department of Surgery from 1984 to January 2005.

His progressive approach, honest but gentle bedside manner, and stalwart surgical skills brought patients in, and the center became busier and very well known. The center is

Through the years Dr. Somers has met with physicians and hospital administrators as far away as San Francisco and St. Louis and as nearby as Trenton and Toms River, NJ, to offer guidance and to help them organize forums on how to develop a multidisciplinary breast center. In addition, he has presented at the National Consortium of Breast Centers on the same topic. "They all want to know how to do it," he remarks. And with good reason: annually, more than 182,000 women in the United States are diagnosed with invasive breast cancer. "That's a lot of women!" he declares.

"Part of the increased prevalence of the disease and prediction that one in eight

"For my patients, though, their worries and anxieties are very important. I have to give them assurance and optimism, and project that optimism, but honest optimism."

currently under expansion and hopes to increase annual mammography screenings from its current 12,000-13,000 to 40,000 annually. "That's just annual screening, not treating symptomatic people coming in to get screening," says Dr. Somers. The center, now with three breast surgeons, including Somers, sees about 2,500 new breast patients annually and treats more than 300 new cancers a year.

women will have invasive breast cancer in her lifetime is from the actual increase in lifetime expectancy of a woman," Somers explains. "We do get to diagnose women younger and sooner because the screening is finding completely curable DCIS (Ductal Carcinoma In Situ) that is not quite life threatening. Mammography certainly has changed a lot of things by detecting smaller tumors and at an early stage."

"Mammography has made people come in here who wouldn't have come for any examination. The breast cancer movement in general has made women unafraid to talk about their cancers. Women now come to our office with any kind of breast problem they are worried about."

"I see the future treatment of this disease in medicines that are aimed specifically at cancer cells rather that at any group of cells." he says, leaning back in his chair. "There will be changes, and science will make those medicines better. The cure rate and increase in survivors is systemic therapy and early detection," he says, getting up from his chair. He walks two short steps and flips a switch on the wall, lighting up four mammogram films displayed side by side.

"Women need to know breast cancer is curable, especially in today's world with the screening." He retrieves a pen from his jacket pocket and begins tapping the mammograms, taking a minute to look them over. "You know," he says thoughtfully, "some women don't want to get a mammogram because they're afraid it might find cancer. I say to them, 'If you're afraid there might be cancer there, if it's there, don't you think you better find it? Face it. Go after it. And if it's not there stop worrying about it.' For my patients, though, their worries and anxieties are very important. I have to give them assurance and optimism, and project that optimism, but honest optimism. As the doctor I have to say to them 'I do understand your worry.'"

"Nothing makes me happier than when my patients return for their annual check-up healthy and happy to be alive."

Dr. Somers sits back down and stretches his arms out across his desk. "My goal as the breast surgeon is to remove the primary cancer correctly with lumpectomy or mastectomy and sentinel node or node dissections. What I do with the breast saves the quality of life for my patient. To most women, the general assumption is that quality of life means preserving both their breasts. Their quality of life can increase for them by having a lumpectomy or mastectomy with immediate reconstruction. Some women, for a variety of reasons, say their quality of life is peace of mind from worrying whether their cancer might come back. They don't want a lumpectomy, they want both breasts removed. And you know, it wouldn't be what I would choose particularly," he admits, tapping his pen on his desk, "But some women do choose it. As their doctor I'm supposed to be sensitive to that and support their decision."

In recent months, Dr. Somers has considered gradually scaling back his office hours. After forty plus years in the trenches fighting and treating breast cancer, no one can blame him for wanting to take some time to enjoy his life.

"No other career could afford me greater satisfaction and gratification. Nothing makes me happier than when my patients return for their annual check-up healthy and happy to be alive. It is a reward that is absolutely priceless to me." The buttons of his jacket pop with pride.

It is this unique combination of a compassionate, understanding breast surgeon and dedicated teacher that has earned Dr. Somers the highest respect in his field.

Beth Cravitz Manusov
Breast Cancer Survivor

Beth comes to her front door smiling, dressed in gray sweats and a T-shirt, her hair pulled back in a lavender bandana. She is carrying Hannah, her seven-month old daughter, on her hip. Taking one look at this vibrant, beautiful, healthy young woman, it's hard to imagine she once battled breast cancer. But she did when she was only twenty-six years old. She was in a thriving career as a senior corporate accountant and had an active social life. The world was at her doorstep. All of that changed, suddenly and drastically, after she felt a lump in her breast. Her once-bright future turned dark and full of uncertainty.

Beth's journey began on a late Saturday evening in October 1998 when she came home from a concert. "You know how you lift off your shirt?" she explains while giving Hannah a bottle. "And my hand just stopped because there was something hard, right on the side of my right breast. Immediately I thought that feeling was not right, that there was something wrong. It was a shocking feeling."

Anxious and upset, Beth called her general practitioner the next day. "The doctor didn't say, 'Oh, come in and let me check it out,'" she says. "The doctor asked if I was getting my period soon and I was within a week or so. She told me a lot of young women my age get lumpy and hard breasts right before their periods so it's probably nothing. She said, 'Just see if it goes away after your period. Don't worry about it.' "

But Beth did worry and shared her anxiety with her mother, Pat, who immediately made an appointment for her daughter with a breast surgeon. "The doctor examined me and thought it was a cyst so she tried to aspirate it but nothing came out," describes Beth. "After a series of ultrasounds they said it was probably a fibroadenoma, a benign breast lump. But because it was so big and uncomfortable for me the doctor said it should be removed. It was scary, but it wasn't that scary because she said it was benign."

While trying to coax a burp out of Hannah, Beth recalls an urgent phone call she received from her doctor in the middle of her workday. "She called me and said I should come right over to her office. I asked if I should bring someone with me," Beth says, her voice quivering slightly, "and she said my parents should meet me there. A girlfriend from work drove me because I was so shaken up I couldn't drive."

With her heart pounding and her parents at her side, Beth was told she had a cystosarcoma phyllodes tumor. "They always come up benign on a needle biopsy but it's only when they excise the tumor that they find out what it really is," she explains. "Phyllodes tumors are usually benign, but mine was the one quarter of one percent that was highly malignant." Though phyllodes tumors are very rare, the cancerous ones usually occur in younger women; nobody knows why. Phyllodes tumors do not respond to traditional chemotherapy or radiation and the only treatment was mastectomy.

Beth's breast surgeon recommended she remove her right breast. "It's one thing to find out you have this rare form of breast cancer," says Beth, bouncing baby Hannah on her knees. "It's another thing to find out there is no other option than to have a mastectomy when you're twenty-six years old. My parents and I went to get other opinions trying to find out if there was another option, but everything came up the same, mastectomy."

"The whole thing was mentally and emotionally a blur. In the blink of an eye I found out I had a life-threatening disease and had to prepare for body-altering surgery. My whole world was upside-down. It didn't seem real. I remember I felt like I was in a fog, like I was watching a movie of a sad event happening in someone else's life, not mine. But it was my life and it was just so hard to believe," she says. "I thought to myself, 'Oh my God, I'm going to die and I haven't even had a serious boyfriend yet.' I totally saw my mortality when I really was just starting to live. I remember driving in my car and seeing people being happy, walking and running, and I would think, 'How could these people go on with their lives when life is so unfair? How can that be?' I remember all of these feelings lasting until after my mastectomy."

Beth underwent a mastectomy with immediate breast reconstruction. "It took me about six weeks to recover. And then it was back to work. You have to go back to your life," she says matter of factly. "But at the same time I thought it wasn't fair that I wasn't getting any kind of other treatment. It felt like maybe it was just too soon for me to go back to my life as usual."

With the desire to have further treatment gnawing at her mentally, Beth contacted experts at Dana Farber Cancer Institute in Boston, Fox Chase Cancer Center, and Hospital of the University of Pennsylvania, both in Philadelphia. But all the doctors said the same thing. The cancer didn't spread and her lymph nodes were clear. There was nothing else to do.

Doctors at Fox Chase encouraged Beth to have genetic testing because of her Ashkenazi Jewish background. She tested positive for BRCA1, one of the three common breast cancer mutations found in Ashkenazi Jews. "They told me it was kind of funny that I tested positive for BRCA1," she laughs, "because they hadn't any records of anyone having that gene and having a cysto phyllodes sarcoma, so they couldn't correlate the two. They said there was no link between the two but I don't believe it," she says, shaking her head.

Beth's paternal grandmother and paternal great-grandmother had ovarian cancer, so she always knew she was at risk for it. As a carrier of BRCA1, she was now at an even greater risk and the chance of getting ovarian cancer became a disconcerting reality. "I wanted to get my ovaries out *immediately*," she says. "I was much more afraid of getting ovarian cancer. It's deadlier than breast cancer. I actually went to my gynecologist and scheduled the surgery. I was still unmarried and wanted to have kids, but figured that I could always adopt."

"Since the risk for ovarian cancer increases after you're thirty-five, it was recommended I 'sit tight' for a few years. But," she sighs, "because I was a carrier of BRCA1 and still at high risk for breast cancer, it was recommended that I remove my left breast." So in 2000, when she was twenty-eight, Beth had a mastectomy of her left breast. "Well, it was reliving a nightmare," she remarks of the surgery.

To cope with the rollercoaster of emotions and anxieties, Beth sought support from different breast cancer groups after her first mastectomy. "It just took me a long time to get past it," she says. "I had to go through different stages. For me I kind of felt like I was alone because I was so young and also single. A lot of the support groups had women with husbands and children," she continues. "But I was still glad I went. Breast cancer isn't the kind of disease you have to suffer with alone."

Michael wholeheartedly agrees, "Beth was less than half the age of anyone else I knew of, or heard of, who had breast cancer," he says. "Learning that Beth had breast cancer didn't tarnish the positive attributes that attracted me, it really added to them. I knew she must possess a world-class fighting spirit. And what a rare and valuable trait that is."

Beth and Michael married in 2004. She was thirty-two and he was forty. Seven months later Beth became pregnant. "It was the biggest relief ever. And here she is,"

> "In the blink of an eye I found out I had a life-threatening disease and had to prepare for body-altering surgery."

For several years she was active in the Komen Philadelphia Race for the Cure. She was in charge of their pledge donations and also volunteered for the Linda Creed Foundation, a Philadelphia based breast cancer non-profit organization. Beth quickly became a spokesperson for breast cancer survivors.

In 2001, Beth met her future husband, Michael. "I had to tell him right away," she says of her breast cancer. "Michael asked me out on a date but I couldn't go because it was a big planning day before the Komen Race for the Cure. He wanted to do something and I said to him, 'I'm doing this. This is a BIG deal, I'm a survivor, so I can't miss it.' He later said that was one of the reasons why he liked me so much, because I took a negative and turned it into a positive."

Beth beams proudly, bouncing Hannah up and down on her lap while Hannah giggles with delight.

"I have done the entire journey and run the gamut of emotions and grieving. But unfortunately, my mother still hasn't gotten over it. And my dad has issues of guilt."

Through genetic testing, Beth's family learned that she and her younger sister, inherited the BRCA1 gene from their father. Beth's sister also had breast cancer, a different type and a few years after Beth's second mastectomy. "I never even knew he had these feelings until my mom told me some time later. For my mom, it's all still right there in front of her face. It still affects her mentally." And when it happened with

"You better appreciate your life because something can happen at any moment and you have to live for today."

my sister," her voice trails off. "She thinks it should've been her to get the breast cancer. She always used to say, 'Why does this have to happen to my two girls, why not me?' She used to tell me, 'Oh, you'll never understand until you have a child what it can do to you.' And now that I'm a mother I fully understand why it was so difficult for her, and remains so to this day."

"You know, I was so upset I had breast cancer so young, but now I'm glad it happened that way because I see now that once you have children, something like that takes your focus off of the family, and it can be harder, much harder. I worry a lot," she says looking at Hannah. "So, she's a girl. But I told her pediatrician about my illness. I waited until her one-month checkup. I was

kind of proud of myself for waiting a whole month," she smiles, pleased with herself.

It has been seven and half years since Beth's breast cancer. "If I'm having a bad day or something is bothering me, now sometimes I have to consciously bring it up and remind myself I shouldn't get upset over such minutia. It was such an awful thing having breast cancer, and I really just tried to grow from it. You know, make lemonade when life gives you lemons," she shrugs, "and realize, you know what, you're not going to live forever. You better appreciate your life because something can happen at any moment and you have to live for today." Hannah gazes up at her mother and smiles in agreement.

Beth N. Peshkin, MS, CGC
Genetic Counselor

It's pleasantly cool and quiet on the fourth floor of the Harris Building — a welcome contrast to the sweltering, humid air outside bustling downtown Georgetown. Beth is one of the few staff members in during lunch hour. She walks briskly from the waiting area down the hall to her office, where, once inside, she shuffles around some papers on her small conference table. When she's done, Beth smoothes out her skirt and takes a seat at the table. Beth has worked at Georgetown University since 1995, her professional journey beginning as a genetic counselor. She has

advanced impressively, and is now an associate professor of oncology and senior genetic counselor.

"I was always interested in science, but never wanted to go to medical school, so genetic counseling is a good blend of things." She glances up, her eyes glistening with the warm blue hues of the Caribbean Sea. From 1990 to 1991, between college and graduate school, Beth worked for the National Cancer Institute's 1-800-4CANCER information hotline, which developed her interest in cancer.

Beth earned a Master of Science degree in medical genetics from the University of Wisconsin, Madison, in 1993 and Certification in Genetic Counseling from the American Board of Genetic Counseling in 1996.

"I knew that I wanted to do adult cancer genetics. Genetic counseling appealed to me because it seemed the ideal blend of providing complex medical information in addition to supportive counseling and advocacy. At the time there were only a few counselors in the country doing it. Most genetic counselors practiced in a prenatal setting." She laughs, "I always said I'd sooner wait tables than take a job not doing cancer genetics." Her first job was with Memorial Sloan-Kettering in New York City.

Beth works in a multi-disciplinary research setting at Lombardi Comprehensive Cancer Center, where most of the clinical, research, and educational programs she conducts involve women at high risk for hereditary breast or ovarian cancers. "When I started here we were asking very basic research questions, like who's interested in testing in terms of demographics and psychological profiles, versus who declines testing." This was around the time when the BRCA1/2 genes were identified in 1995.

"The cloning of the BRCA1 and BRCA2 genes was a huge discovery, and had important historical significance because breast cancer isn't caused exclusively by genes." Beth's voice is gentle and soothing. "But here, genes were identified and it gave credence to what wasn't universally accepted. Many people had observed that breast cancer ran in families; there were skeptics about the fact that gene mutations would ever be identified to explain that, or that a test would become available to detect those gene changes, so the impact has been tremendous."

In her fifteen years as a genetic counselor, Beth has had many occasions to meet

"...genetic testing allows women to make medical choices that were not available to their mothers and grandmothers."

relatives from multiple generations in families. "The elders express their dreams for the younger generation, in particular, that knowledge is power and genetic testing allows women to make medical choices that were not available to their mothers and grandmothers."

Beth stands up, walks to a filing cabinet, and begins thumbing through a drawer. She finds what she's looking for and brings it over to the table. In her hand is a copy of a report from a large study she collaborated on, assessing the impact of genetic counseling and testing of self-referred, newly diagnosed women.

"The process of genetic counseling is to help people understand their cancer risk and management options," she explains. "In this study we found that women newly diagnosed with breast cancer who tested positive for a BRCA1 or BRCA2 mutation often chose to have bilateral mastectomies. In other words, women who were candidates for breast conservation therapy such as lumpectomy or radiation, or a unilateral mastectomy chose bilateral mastectomies in order to reduce their risk of a second breast cancer. We also found a fair number of women who tested negative for BRCA1/2 mutations also had bilateral mastectomies, which suggests that there are a lot of reasons why women consider that procedure. Maybe their cancer wasn't found on a mammogram, or they've had multiple

biopsies. Another possibility is that they learn through the process of genetic counseling, based on their personal and family history, that they are at high risk, even though they didn't test positive for a gene mutation."

As a result of this study, Beth and her colleagues are doing a second study entitled, "Genetic Counseling for Newly Diagnosed Breast Cancer Patients." This study, she says, will likely affect clinical practice. "We're working with surgeons at Georgetown, Mount Sinai School of Medicine in New York, and Hackensack University Medical Center in New Jersey, as well as with a surgeon in private practice in Maryland.

"This study will give us a good indicator of all potentially eligible patients and see what the

impact is for those patients that get rapid genetic counseling versus those who receive usual care." By rapid counseling, Beth refers to a woman who is selected by the study to undergo genetic counseling soon after her breast cancer diagnosis, before making a surgery decision. Usual care means that study participants are seen at any time after the diagnosis, based on their doctor's referral and/or patient preferences.

This study is not without its critics, as some clinicians feel it is too overwhelming to approach women about genetic counseling after just being diagnosed with breast cancer. "This is rather paternalistic," Beth says, frowning in disagreement. "The other school

of thought says every woman should have this opportunity for counseling. Some women want this information at the time of diagnosis to make a surgical decision." She folds her delicate hands together and rests them on the table in front of her. "I think this study will tell us the best way to approach women about genetic testing, and whether or not it truly is an overwhelming time emotionally for them."

More than 400,000 people have tested clinically for BRCA1/2 since the mid-1990s, and the test results can be pivotal for managing cancer risk. "Both of the studies we have conducted show that in newly diagnosed patients, genetic testing may impact their initial surgery decision making, particularly if they test positive for a BRCA1/2 mutation. In terms of detection, we now have evidence that for women at high risk, breast MRIs may pick up cancers that mammography would not have and this is very, very encouraging." She leans forward, excited. "We also know that many women who have tested positive have their ovaries removed, so we hope to see mortality from ovarian cancer declining in women with BRCA mutations." This declining mortality rate, in her opinion, will be a very significant impact of BRCA1/2 testing.

Like a teacher reviewing the steps to a complex math equation, Beth carefully dissects the facts which have shaped her opinion. "We have very poor screening for ovarian cancer. Genetic testing is the medical community's best tool to identify women with high risk of ovarian cancer," she explains. "Many women who test BRCA positive don't have a family history of ovarian cancer and would have had no other means of knowing that they are at increased risk. This is pushing the agenda for better ovarian cancer screening because we are now identifying who these women are."

She takes some of her wavy light brown hair and puts it behind her ear. "We know that MRIs for high-risk women may be effective at detecting early-stage breast cancers, but we don't have a comparable screening test for detecting ovarian cancer in its earliest stages. We don't want it to be that the best we can tell women is they should remove their ovaries, but this is exactly what the medical community is doing right now."

Beth says many young women, BRCA positive, aged thirty-five to forty-five are choosing

potential drawbacks. The one with the most hype, she explains, is the health insurance discrimination issue, but she is quick to point out most of the reported problems in this arena are anecdotal and not well documented. And now that federal legislation exists to prevent health insurance and employment discrimination, this should become less of an issue.

The real drawbacks that exist, she says, are being emotionally unprepared to handle positive results, and also serving as the gatekeeper of information when deciding, if, when, and how to share this information with family members about their own genetic risks. "This is why I worry when the medical community presents it as a simple blood, or

"No matter how patients come away with the information intellectually, it can still be hard for them emotionally."

prophylactic oophorectomy, removal of the ovaries. "It's been really tough for these women," she sympathizes, "to navigate through the medical system with their physicians, only to find very troubling quality of life issues related to menopause. It would be much better if we had good screening which detected early-stage ovarian cancers. Or better yet, some way of preventing it entirely."

Beth is mindful that while BRCA testing may have reduced breast and ovarian cancer deaths, the process of genetic testing has

now, saliva test, because the ramifications often are not immediately apparent. No matter how patients come away with the information intellectually, it can still be hard for them emotionally," she confides. "I often tell a patient who has a positive test result to give themselves a window of time to react. Sometimes when they tell family members, those relatives don't feel it has many implications for them. That can be difficult for the patient to cope with. Other times the patient can't get around the guilt. It might be surprising, but it happens."

Beth shares a story about a patient, a father of three daughters who are all BRCA positive. The father himself received positive test results. "While the results had no medical implications for him, his angst about having passed it down to his daughters, including one who had cancer, was very powerful. It was one of the most emotionally wrenching situations for me," she remembers in a voice just above a whisper. "I thought about how my own dad would feel. I was glad my patient got this information in this setting," she says glancing around her office, "and not just in a regular doctor's office."

Within the next decade, other patients like this father and his daughters will come into Beth's office and receive a more integrated, individualized risk assessment that is not just based on the gene mutation. "Right now we test women for BRCA1/2 and then pull the range of risks for cancer based on a variety of studies. What we would like to do in the future is to do a panel of tests, not just for the major breast cancer genes, but also test for genetic variations that may modify that risk."

"We would also take into consideration classic reproductive factors: how old was the patient when she had her first period, when did she have her first child, did she breastfeed. We would mathematically combine all this information to come up with a more precise risk. It would also help us understand why we don't see the same pattern of cancer within the same family."

In the course of her career Beth has been privileged to counsel nearly eight hundred patients. "No two patients are alike," she observes. "Their reasons for getting tested may be similar but the context of why they're in my office makes each situation unique. It's remarkable how relatively well they integrate this information into their life. Research has shown when a mutation is known within a family, the women who don't undergo testing have higher anxiety or distress levels than those women who receive positive or negative test results. This is probably due to the lingering uncertainty of their risk," she explains.

A lot of the women who come in here with breast cancer ask that existential question, 'Why me?' " Beth says. "For a lot of women, testing positive isn't the complete answer to that question, but for some it is such important knowledge, because they now realize it is something they had no control over."

Beth folds her arms across her body and slowly reclines in her chair. "This is the fabric of genetic counseling that I think is valuable. People realize it is more than a piece of paper with a result. I am amazed and touched at the resiliency, courage, and sensitivity of patients who have gone through the process of genetic testing, and how well they cope with this information. Information I've given them that is, undoubtedly, life changing."

Carolyn O'Donnell
Remembered by her surviving son, James Grupenhoff

The weather in Coconut Grove, FL, where James Grupenhoff lives, is picture-perfect for this spring afternoon. The sun shines bright in the midday sky, and the temperature is a comfortable 80 degrees. James lives in a charming, quiet, residential neighborhood here, just a stone's throw from the dazzle and excitement of Miami. James and his wife, Susan, are expecting their first child due next month. Like most first-time parents, they look forward to their new roles with excitement and trepidation. For James, fatherhood marks the beginning of a new and exciting journey. A journey he hopes will bring endless opportunities to pass down his mother

Carolyn's love and wisdom. Carolyn's life was taken by breast cancer in January 2004.

James heads to his backyard, a small tropical oasis landscaped with lush vegetation. Brightly colored flowers are blooming everywhere. He pulls up a chair around the wrought-iron patio table, and makes himself comfortable. "My mother was a very nurturing person. Always very positive on her outlook on life," he says, settling in. "She was also very reinforcing. I remember as a child she always gave me encouragement, and allowed me and my brother to do things we felt strongly about. She never stopped us from doing things we wanted to. She truly was magnanimous, never allowing her emotions and personal feelings about people to get in the way of how she treated them. Some people," James chuckles, "say she was even too nice. She always treated people well, even if they didn't deserve it."

Carolyn O'Donnell was a professor of speech and theatre at Rowan University in Glassboro, NJ, where she worked for more than twenty-seven years until her death from metastatic breast cancer. "My mother loved working with young people, and teaching was her way of passing on her love of the theatre. She never approached her job like she was training these students to be professional actors. So whether her students had ambitions to go to Hollywood or Broadway, or were simply in her class learning to enrich their lives a little more, she taught acting and theatre as that true essence of an art form. She always reminded her students that they should take what they've learned in her class and apply it in whatever way that works for them out in the world."

In the 1980s, Carolyn fulfilled a longtime dream and founded her own theatre company, which was in residence at the university. It wasn't long before Stageworks Theatre Company became her second full-time job. Stageworks provided Carolyn another venue to show off her gifts as a talented actress and director, and represented her grassroots efforts to bring live, original theatre to the rural communities which lay just beyond Rowan's doorsteps.

Over time, with state and private funding, the theatre company blossomed, performing its thought-provoking plays throughout the state's twenty-one counties.

James gets up from his chair and walks inside to the living room. He reaches for a picture resting on a hutch. There is James and his mother, their arms around each other. She is very pretty, his mother, and very much full of life. An enormous smile is splashed across Carolyn's face, and her rich blue eyes sparkle with the strong bond of love between a devoted mother and her son.

James stares at the photograph with sentimental eyes. "Although my mother had been at Rowan for twenty-seven years," he says, looking up, "she had wanted to continue teaching there. She wasn't able to do it, though. The cancer consumed her and she had to stop working. After she died," he explains, gently putting the photograph back in its place, "my brother and I established a scholarship fund at the university in her memory. Her family contributed to it also. Every semester we award money to a student who is studying theatre. It's our attempt to continue her legacy and that unique philosophy she brought to her teaching."

By the time Carolyn was diagnosed with breast cancer in January 2001, she was divorced from James's father and living on her own in Philadelphia. "Because we lived far away from each other, we didn't see each other for more than a few weeks a year," says James. "When she found out she had breast cancer, my brother and I would talk a lot on the phone with her and give her support that way. But there is a limit to how much you can do if you don't live near somebody in that situation," he says, shaking his head. "It was difficult."

James and his brother visited their mother as often as their lives would permit, but for a large part of her illness, Carolyn was on her own. During that time, James says, she continued living her healthy lifestyle, eating a macrobiotic diet, and taking organic vitamins. Raised Catholic, she rarely went to

"It took me time to realize that I couldn't do that anymore. I just have to hope that I've already learned the things I need to know in order to make certain decisions on my own. I still have my dad. I rely on him for many things, but it's just different things."

Susan walks into the room holding a tall glass of ice water, her belly swelling with the new life inside. Carefully, she eases into the sofa next to James. "I've had some friends that have lost parents for the first time," James says, taking Susan's hand in his, "and I

"My mother loved working with young people, and teaching was her way of passing on her love of the theatre."

church. "But towards the end of her life, my mother found religion again," James recalls. "She started going back to church and praying. She actively pursued every different type of treatment to save her life, even if it came down to praying."

James rests his large, handsome frame on the living room sofa. Folding his hands together, he says, "The hardest part for me after my mother died was making that transition. For about a year, I wanted to call her whenever I would think of something or have a question about our family history or how I should go about doing something.

tell them having other people tell you how that experience was for them will only transfer a little. There is nothing that can prepare you for the death of a parent until you experience it yourself. Looking back, I think my mother raised me in a way that I could probably stand to be a little tougher in how I deal with the world," he says. "But it's this special relationship I had with her that makes me who I am." He softly pats Susan's belly. "We're expecting our first child in a month," says James, smiling at his wife. "I am looking forward to passing on my mother's wit and wisdom to the next generation."

Generosa Grana, MD
Oncologist

The sound of ambulance sirens resonates through the windows of Dr. Generosa Grana's office at Cooper University Hospital in Camden, NJ, while she sits at her computer reading through emails. It's Tuesday, and Dr. Grana, director of the Cooper Cancer Institute and head of Division of Hematology/Oncology, will spend the better part of her day here taking care of administrative duties. On other weekdays she meets with patients at her offices in Stratford and Voorhees, NJ. As she clicks off her computer and takes a seat at a small conference table, Dr. Grana jokes about her unplanned journey to becoming a highly recognized expert on breast cancer.

During her early childhood in Galicia, a small, rural village of about fifty families in the northwestern part of Spain, Dr. Grana was only exposed to two professions. "They were the priest and the physician," she says, a small hint of her native Spanish language in her speech. "And I remember my grandmother was ill. This was in 1965, there were no cars, no driving roads," she shakes her head smiling, "and I remember going on a horse with my mother to pick up the doctor. We brought him to our house on the horse, he treated my grandmother, and then we brought him back on the horse, that's how prehistoric it was. So that was one of my first experiences with people of careers," she chuckles at the memory.

At the age of ten, Grana's family immigrated to America and settled in Indiana where her father worked in the large steel industry. It was a series of events, she says, that led her

to Cooper University Hospital. Dr Grana did her medical residency at Temple University in Philadelphia, PA, after attending Northwestern University Medical College. And while at Temple she did an oncology rotation at Fox Chase Cancer Center also in Philadelphia. She then did an oncology fellowship and then a joint post doctoral fellowship in preventive oncology at Fox Chase and Temple. "I knew I was interested in women's health, but I came to breast cancer because of the mentors I acquired at Fox Chase. They really inspired me and fostered my interest in breast cancer." Dr. Grana's interest in genetics and the hereditary aspects of cancer was sparked by her involvement in a breast cancer program for high-risk women at Fox Chase.

In 1993, after finishing a post doctoral fellowship, Dr. Grana looked for a permanent position at area hospitals. Cooper offered her a unique opportunity to pursue the three things she wanted to do most. "I knew I wanted to take care of women with breast cancer. I wanted to develop a program like Fox Chase's in terms of high risk and genetics and I was very interested in working with minority populations. I was interested in Hispanics, obviously, and I wanted to work with underserved minorities. Cooper gave me support to pursue these three interests and I've been here ever since," she says with a pleasant smile.

"With breast cancer, I take care of the woman, but I also look at the hereditary aspects of her cancer and then reach out into her family," explains Grana. "The patient

38

is the first one I meet, but then I begin meeting her siblings and her children who are coming in for genetic testing. I like that involvement with her family and her spouse. It often becomes working as a unit, and that's what I enjoy most out of everything I do."

Patients meet with Dr. Grana after they've learned they have breast cancer. "Some patients may have heard about breast cancer before or may have done some reading on the Internet and are petrified because of

conference table with her hands. "And then I talk about what we need to do to get there. If it's metastatic disease I'm very honest to say, 'We may not be able to cure this but we have a lot of treatment options.' But my first job, though, is giving calm and slowing the emotional process. And it does happen. The other thing, it doesn't all have to be accomplished in one visit," she acknowledges. "I can give some information the first visit, then do some tests and have the patient come back and discuss things again. I spend a lot of time

"I think the first job of the oncologist is to reassure and calm the patient so that we can exchange information."

what they've read," she says, pulling her pinstriped pantsuit jacket closer to her body. "Some patients are very well educated and informed and others are not so informed. But it's always a very emotional laden first visit. Women, often, don't come alone; they come with a spouse, a friend or they even bring the entire family."

"I think the first job of the oncologist is to reassure and calm the patient so that we can exchange information. We have to make decisions so if the patient is so overwrought and anxious there's not going to be any great exchange of information. If it's early-stage breast cancer, the first thing I tell the patient is, 'This is a curable disease.' I lay that on the table first." Grana gently pats the small

with my patients, and these visits are long visits. Sometimes patients will call and say they still need more information and then we sit down again together."

As an oncologist specializing in the genetic factors of breast cancer, educating women about their breast cancer risk and their available treatment options is an essential and important priority for Grana. "I think the issues are different for everybody. My fears and my concerns may not be a patient's fears and concerns," she says, raising her eyebrows. "With some women it's how they handle risk. Some are really worried about their risk. It's on their mind all the time. These women are more likely to have bilateral mastectomies," she notes. "There

are many women, though, that are much less concerned about their risk. They can go for their yearly mammogram and can just put it out of their mind after that. By and large that is why we give women treatment options. It really is an individual choice."

"But what's most interesting to me as I've done this work is how the family history impacts the decision making. When you see how women cope with their risk and how they come to their medical decisions, it's also affected by what they've seen," she adds. "If they've seen ugly cancers in their family, if they've seen death, it is going to affect their thoughts and their actions. There is also a difference in the decisions women make based on the age of their children," she continues. "Now, I have not studied this," she says, motioning with her hands, "but I

see mothers of very young children more likely to be very aggressive with chemotherapy and their surgery because their mission is to do everything possible to stay alive for their children. I think the older woman may have the same fears but she doesn't have the same pressure, her children are grown."

Dr. Grana encourages her patients with young children to communicate with them about what they are going through. "Children are much deeper than we give them credit for," she acknowledges, "and often times they have fears they keep in check. I encourage moms who are getting chemotherapy to bring their kids, five, ten, twelve years old, with them so their kids know where mom is going. So they know that she is not going to some torture

chamber. The children can meet the nurses that are taking care of their mom and realize this is a safe, warm environment."

Regardless of a woman's age, Dr. Grana is a fervent believer in educating all women, young and old, about their breast cancer risk and risk reductions. "It's very important. Young women really need to know that breast cancer is a common disease, but if caught early it is a highly treatable disease. My most important message to young women is to understand their risk, to be

proactive and to discuss with their family practitioner what strategies are right for them. My message for older women is the same, but to also understand the other health issues facing them, because breast cancer is just one of them and it's definitely not the biggest one."

Dr. Grana leans forward, resting her elbows on the table. "Many women today are so breast cancer phobic that they lose perspective on the bigger health issues. They know a lot about breast cancer and early detection. But I

> "It was a Friday night, I had looked at my mammogram and it clearly looked like a cancer. I was sure it was going to be the worst kind and that I would need chemotherapy, and I was not going to be there for my kids."

don't think we really educate women about greater health risks, like cardiovascular disease, diabetes, obesity, or even osteoporosis. The biggest cancer killer of women today is lung cancer yet we don't talk about it," she nods. "So I think we need to put breast cancer in its rightful place."

The passion in her voice rises as Dr. Grana discusses her work and the future of breast cancer treatment throughout the world. "I think the next five to ten years are going to be really exciting. The Europeans are studying the concept that maybe you can remove all the tumor with just a core biopsy process, now is that enough?" she asks, shrugging her shoulders. "The Europeans are also looking at delivering radiation right in the operating room."

"I think ten years from now we're going to look back and things will be very different. We're finding more cancers earlier that may not have led to clinical diagnoses in a different generation. There is clearly an increase in DCIS because of mammography, but I think the international trend suggests that there is an increase in breast cancer.

So, why is that? Is it environmental? Is it reproductive? There is a lot more research that needs to be done, but I do think mammography has changed the face of the disease."

A year and half ago, Dr. Grana was, herself, diagnosed with DCIS after micro-calcifications were found on her annual mammogram. She learned firsthand the emotional trauma experienced by her breast cancer patients. "It was a Friday night, I had looked at my mammogram and it clearly looked like a cancer. I was sure it was going to be the worst kind and that I would need chemotherapy, and I was not going to be there for my kids." Dr. Grana has a daughter in college and twin sons in high school. "All of those thoughts crossed my mind, so when the pathologist told me the diagnosis was DCIS, I really thought it was a gift." She smiles in relief. Her own breast cancer journey has had a profound impact on her patient interaction.

"I always thought I was compassionate," says Grana, "but now I have a whole new sense of the fear, the uncertainty, and the difficulty of the decision-making process. I find that I spend a lot more time now discussing options. Interestingly, before, if a patient told me, 'I want bilateral mastectomies,' I would say, 'Go for it,' I'm never opposed to bilateral mastectomies or even a mastectomy. Now I really go over backwards to make sure my patients fully understand the process, understand reconstruction, because I know that I was surprised by some of the things that I went through as a patient, and I think women need to be prepared for those things. They need to have realistic expectations. I give more information and I think I'm more understanding of the things they're going through. I don't think doctors prepare patients for post-surgery. I was not prepared for it. The drains were miserable," she frowns, "So I spend more time making sure women understand all of their options."

Dr. Grana is internationally recognized for her breast cancer expertise. Yet despite the notoriety, she is completely unpretentious. Besides being named a Top Doc by *Philadelphia, New Jersey Monthly,* and *South Jersey* magazines, Grana was recently awarded the 2009 Beacon of Hope by the Komen for the Cure Philadelphia affiliate.

Dr. Grana remains unusually modest about her many professional achievements. "I'm just doing my job," she smiles graciously. Her warmth and unwavering compassion and commitment are the reasons her patients, staff, and colleagues admire her so much.

"The most rewarding part of my work," she leans back in her chair, "is dealing with the patient and her family as they're going through this diagnosis and sharing in their experience. You know it's amazing that people will let you into their life at such a point and to let you be a part of it," she says, brushing away a few strands of her dark brown hair from her eyes. "And yet the most difficult part of my job is being a part of that experience. It's one and the same."

"It's wonderful when I have patients that do well with early-stage breast cancer and I see them year after year as survivors. But there are still so many battles that are lost," she says, her voice saddened. "I see many young women dying, and I have to deal with that–preparing her, preparing her family. It's very, very difficult, not just for me but also for my staff," she shakes her head, remorseful. "The whole office really mourns. It's a huge loss for all of us."

"But what I continue to love about taking care of women with breast cancer is that it's women's health," Grana says, smiling. "It's the ability to work with the patient and her family. And it's the ability to be part of a team. You don't take care of breast cancer or any cancer, for that matter, as a lone individual. It is truly a team endeavor of physicians of multiple disciplines, surgery, radiation, medical oncology. It's nursing and social work," she adds. "And I really love that about what I do."

Faye Feldman, CRNP, BC
Breast Cancer Nurse Practitioner

Before she calls it a day, Faye takes one last walk through the Infusion Center in the Marlene and Stewart Greenebaum Cancer Center at the University of Maryland Medical Center in Baltimore. As she says her goodnights, she tenderly pats the hands of patients and staff she passes by. Sometimes she stops and speaks quietly with a patient she knows, offering some private words of encouragement. Her journey to a career as a breast cancer nurse practitioner began shortly after she earned a Master's Degree as

a family nurse practitioner from the University of Maryland-Baltimore.

"After I finished graduate school I was trying to figure out where to go," she says, walking down the hall to the staff lounge. "I wasn't finding anything that I really wanted to do, and I felt like I was trying to sell myself as a nurse practitioner. People didn't know who nurse practitioners were even though we've been around a long time. I ended up interviewing with the doctor I work with now. I really liked her personality and I liked the people that were working here at the time. I thought I'd give it a try, not realizing how much I'd like it."

As she opens the door to the staff lounge, Faye unwraps the stethoscope from around her neck and rests it on the oblong table. While taking a seat, she chatters enthusiastically about her practical training in family and primary care. This job at UMMC is her first working with cancer patients. "Working in oncology is really not like anything else I've done," she explains. "And one of the concerns the staff had was how I would deal with the emotional aspect of oncology. Actually, I myself recognized it when I took the job, because I'm an emotional person anyway," she says, brushing away wisps of her dark brown hair.

As the nurse practitioner, Faye is responsible for meeting with the new patients, reviewing their medical history, doing a basic exam, and then meeting with the doctor. After the

felt a lump in their breast, but usually I see patients who have just had a biopsy. They haven't had surgery yet or anything like that."

After surgery, Faye meets with patients again to discuss their treatment plan whether it's chemotherapy or radiation. "One of the unique parts about my role," she says, as her deep brown eyes brighten with enthusiasm, "is that I do patient education, going through all of the chemotherapy side effects with them, reviewing all of the prescription medicines they're going to take and how to take them. I give them literature to read. I do my best to allay all of their fears. I try to involve the family in the process also. I make sure they have business cards for every doctor so they know who to call for what thing."

"You know, sometimes I think the first visit for them can be very, very overwhelming," says Faye sympathetically. "There are advantages and disadvantages to a multi-disciplinary setting like this because the patient just has

"I do my best to allay all of their fears. I try to involve the family in the process also."

doctor examines the patient, they come up with a course of action for the patient. Established and follow-up patients Faye sees independently.

"I see patients throughout their diagnosis and treatment," she explains in her quiet, soothing voice. "Some of these patients have been referred because of an abnormal mammogram. Others come in because they

to come once and meet everybody, the oncologist, radiologist, and breast surgeon. But then I think when they leave, maybe they're a bit bleary-eyed or confused."

Because of the cancer center's reputation with clinical trials and its convenient location in downtown Baltimore, it attracts a broad spectrum of patients. But, according to Faye, a fair proportion of her patients are indigent, referred through grant programs like the Baltimore City Cancer Program or the Breast and Cervical Grant Program. Both programs provide funds for low-income patients or patients with no insurance. The BCCP, created in 2001 with funding from Maryland's Cigarette Restitution Fund Program, was established to help eliminate cancer deaths in Baltimore through early detection, diagnosis, treatment, and education programs.

"It's a great program," comments Faye. "Otherwise, these people would not get medical treatment. Who would pay for their care?" she says, shrugging her shoulders. "The BCCP pays for everything for breast and cervical cancer treatment including metastatic treatment. The BCCP will also pay for mammograms for low-income women. So we try to get those women in here for their free mammograms," she continues. "Overall, screening has made it so that we are diagnosing breast cancer earlier and earlier. But I see more indigent patients who have not been screened. Their cancers are large and more aggressive. I also see a lot of younger patients too, where their cancer is more aggressive. I think from working here, I see a more biased picture of breast cancer than what is in the general population of Maryland."

A coworker comes into the lounge to make a cup of tea. She and Faye engage in conversation that quickly leads to a brief discussion about breast cancer care. The coworker's comment reminds Faye about a news story she heard several years ago. "It was a news segment that said there is no reason for women to do breast self-exams

because it does very little to help find cancer early." An unsettling look spreads across Faye's face. "I disagree," she says in a sharp tone. "I would advise all women to know their body and do the monthly exam. I would teach young girls who are menstruating how to do a breast self-exam. I really would. I don't think older women do it, but they absolutely should. Women need to understand breast cancer is not a death sentence, even if someone is diagnosed with metastatic disease. You know," she says, smiling, "breast cancer is probably one of the best cancers to have. Not that anyone wants to have it." She motions with her hands like she is stopping a car. "But the disease itself is one that doesn't behave like other cancers, say lung or pancreatic cancers. Breast cancer really isn't a death sentence because there are so many treatment options. A lot of money goes into breast cancer research."

Faye pauses to take a drink from her water bottle. "Patients are always asking me, 'Am I in remission?' We don't use that word remission here," she says, firmly resting the bottle back on the table. "Basically, I tell patients, the further away they get from their initial diagnosis the less chance they have that it can recur. However, if we look at the curve of breast cancer, there is no such thing as breast cancer never recurring. There is no 100 percent you're cured. There is 90-95 percent. There is 95 to 98 percent, a very high cure rate percentage. But patients who have a recurrence are always saying to me, 'I thought I was in remission.' Patients think remission means, 'I'm never going to get cancer again.' Regrettably, it can happen," she says, lowering her voice.

Although she is not the physician, Faye still makes it a point to speak openly with her patients about their breast cancer. "I try and be honest with my patients, but I try also to be…" Faye hesitates for a moment, her dark brown eyes scanning the lounge. "I believe in God," she says, focusing her thoughts. "It might not be the same God that other people believe in, but I try, especially with somebody who has a very strong faith, to be honest and realistic with them. I tell them it's important to pray and believe that things could improve. I tell them they should believe in miracles, but they also need to be realistic," she says gently.

"It's also very important to explain to patients that, yes, people really do live a long time with metastatic cancer. When a patient has metastatic breast cancer, though, I have to say up front that their cancer is not curable. It is treatable, but it's not curable. For some people, that might mean that they live four or five years, for others they can live much longer."

"I always know when we get to the point, or are close to the point where there might be nothing left for a patient. It's hard," she says wiping away teardrops with the palm of her hand, "because the patient realizes too, they're not curable. They know they have fewer options. In the beginning, it was very hard for me, losing patients," she whispers, gazing down into her lap.

"It's different for me compared to people who work with other cancers. My patients live a long time. Some of my patients have had metastatic breast cancer for fifteen to twenty years, so I get to know them and their families very well. I see them through many happy events in their lives. That's why it is so sad when I lose them. It's hard, the hardest part of the job actually. But," she inhales deeply, "compared to other parts of nursing that I've worked in, I feel my patients here are just so much more appreciative. In general, cancer patients are just really different, not all of them, but a lot of them. I help people and they are very appreciative of that and they thank me everyday for everything I do for them." As Faye exhales a peaceful, content feeling washes over her calm, pretty face.

Valerie & Michael Yasner
Breast Cancer Survivor and Husband

It takes less than a minute to see that Valerie and Michael Yasner are no ordinary married couple. After twenty five years of marriage they are still a couple very much in love, and there is an aura of deep admiration, understanding, and mutual respect that surrounds them when they are together. These two are one team, and when Valerie battled breast cancer, Michael put on his own armor to fight the disease along side his wife. This was definitely a journey Val and Michael were going to take together.

As Val and Michael gather around their kitchen table, there is a distraction from Yoffi and Sababa, their Bedlington Terriers, who are romping around outside. The dogs are barking frantically and Val and Michael take turns trying to quiet them down. But Yoffi and Sababa do not want to listen to their parents and continue their commotion. Michael finally concedes, leading the dogs back inside. They lie down quietly, one next to Val and one next to Michael.

A hush falls over the room as Valerie begins to speak. "I was forty-four when I was diagnosed with breast cancer. I felt a lump on a Thursday. I had had a very hectic week and over the weekend I was very much looking forward to a French class that I took in Philadelphia that I had missed the week before because my daughter had broken her nose. On Tuesday, I got in the shower and I felt the lump again. I said, 'You know what Val; you're not going to French class today. You're going to the doctor. He is going to tell you, 'You're crazy.'' So I went to my gynecologist. He felt the lump and said it was probably an adenofibroma, a benign tumor. He did an aspiration biopsy and then

being the surgeon as opposed to the one whose spouse is getting surgery. I knew we had a rough time ahead. But Val and I are activists. We immediately geared up for this upcoming fight against the breast cancer."

Valerie called a local breast surgeon's office she was familiar with. The doctor she knew was away, but the partner could see Val. "I went to see her and told her I wanted a mastectomy," she says, resting her chin on

"Michael went to every chemo treatment with me, every single appointment. That was just how it went."

told me in the next two weeks to get a mammogram. I had just had a mammogram five months before."

Val also told her dear friend, a radiologist at the Hospital of the University of Pennsylvania, about her lump. "She told me to come right down, she'd take a look," Val says, pushing her short, dark brown hair behind her ear. "She did a mammogram and a core biopsy, the next day she called me, it was February thirteenth, and told me that it was breast cancer. She thought it was very small and she gave me a list of people I should see."

"Well, when I first got the phone call from Valerie that the diagnosis was cancer, I had a big sinking feeling in my chest," Michael quietly interjects, pressing his right hand over his heart. "I'm a periodontist. I'm used to

her hand. "And she said that I would have to go somewhere else to get a mastectomy because the lump was so small. The doctor said it was very simple and she would do a lumpectomy. I trusted her and decided I would do what she recommended. The next week I went to the hospital, had the lumpectomy and node dissection. Two days later I came home."

A week later, Val's doctor called with the pathology results. "It didn't look good," Val says as a wistful look comes over her face. "I asked her, 'Are we talking mastectomy?' She said 'Yes,' then I said, 'Okay, let's do two.' The doctor also said there was a plastic surgeon at Jefferson waiting for me in his office. I had to go right then and talk to him," Val sits up straight and gazes over at Michael.

"So I called Michael's office and told him to cancel the rest of his day, I picked him up, and we went to meet the surgeon. Initially I told him I didn't need reconstruction. I just want my breasts removed and that will be that. Years before I had said to myself if I ever got breast cancer, I just would want my breasts removed. You know, they were attached to me; I wasn't so attached to them. I would rather live than have breasts. But the doctor said, 'Val, you're only forty-four years old. You really want to get past it and if your prosthesis is always falling out of your shirt or you're bathing suit... I think you should really think about doing this.' "

"Valerie had very strong and clear ideas about how she wanted to approach this," recalls Michael. "What level of conservative treatment versus the more aggressive treatment she wanted. My job was to simply support her in the decision-making that she was undergoing. You know, to be a good listener at the various doctors' appointments and try to gather the options, remember the details, be able to review and explain things again as we were discussing the options at home," he says. "These were not my decisions to make," he adds, shaking his head back and forth. "I don't think I was ever trying to convince her one way or the other. It was just a matter of making sure that Val was making decisions for the right reasons. I was sort of prodding her to evaluate why she wants things done and what the various physicians were saying about the different options."

Like most things they approach in their marriage, Val and Michael agreed to tell their daughters about Val's breast cancer together, offering them a chance to ask questions and express their own worries or concerns. At the time Maddy was fifteen and Becca was twelve. "We just said it how it was. We didn't make doom and gloom," Val says. "The phone would be ringing. They had heard me talking. It wasn't a secret. In fact, I didn't answer the phone a lot so that I could talk with them and explain to them what was going on."

On March 1, 2002, Val had bilateral mastectomies with breast reconstruction then underwent six months of chemotherapy followed by six weeks of radiation. "The hardest part for me was seeing Valerie having to go through the grueling pace of treatment," explains Michael, looking over at Val. "She had multiple surgical procedures, chemotherapy, and radiation. She was dealing with mortality issues that we never thought we'd be thinking about at this point in our lives, really for both of us. Val was particularly concerned, not so much of the impact on herself, but what the impact would be on the children, if there were long-term complications that were going to be difficult to manage, really a very unselfish approach on her part."

Chemo treatments rendered Val "out of commission," as Michael aptly puts it. "Valerie and I always shared the home responsibilities when our children were very young. There were mommy days and daddy days depending on what day of the week it was," he remembers with a smile. "Now with Val out of commission, I chose to lighten my work schedule to be at home

even more. I had great cooperation from my partners, my staff, and even from patients," he adds. "Everyone was supportive even when I was canceling appointments or canceling work hours on short notice. It just allowed me to help the girls with homework and their school activities, carpools, taking care of the dogs. And I tended to Val like a personal nurse. It all made for some very long days," he sighs.

"Looking back, I'd say people couldn't do enough, they really wanted to help. The support we got was overwhelming and made it a tolerable situation," says Michael. Val adds, "For the most part our kids saw family and friends rally around and help out

with meals, rides, carpools and whatever needed to be done and I think it was important for them to see that."

Even with their extended support system, Michael confesses, it was still a heavy burden for him. "I had a personal coping mechanism. Each day I would try and find a few minutes to catch my breath. Valerie was always the first in bed so it was usually after the kids were tucked in. And the lunches were prepared, and the laundry was put away, and the house was cleaned up."

As Michael ticks off this to do list with his fingers, Val's eyes well up with tears. She gets up from her chair at the table to get some tissues from the kitchen counter. "I'd either take the dogs out for a walk for a few minutes or sit by the fire," he continues, looking over at Val, making sure she is okay. "Maybe talk on the phone to a couple of close friends just to maintain a little communication. Just catching my breath and trying to get some sleep to start the next long day."

Val sits back down. Michael looks into his wife's sparkling green eyes and says, "I'm glad to be done with that," then he tenderly slips her hand into his. They sit quietly like this for a few breaths while Val dabs her tears.

"At some point you're so numb from the chemo," Val says, breaking the silence. "And I think that you just try to do the best you can. So any day that I could be up and dressed somewhat when the kids came home and have them see me making dinner and doing something normal, I did. And that was my motivation. I remember lots of dinners around the table with the girls and not getting up from the table to do the dishes like I normally did," she continues, "but sitting there and talking."

"The children were able to compartmentalize a lot of their feelings and emotions," adds Michael. "At the dinner table we would always discuss Val's next step in treatment, how things were working. We always maintained a positive attitude that this was a problem Mom could get past. It was just going to take some time and effort and a lot of treatment to accomplish that. I think the girls were sensitive to the issues we were

facing but didn't particularly feel threatened for their own well-being."

Just as Michael finishes his sentence, Val begins giggling softly. "I just remembered an incident with my older daughter, Maddy," she says unfolding her hand from Michael's. "She was fifteen, and really she doesn't have a selfish bone in her body. She asked me one day, 'You know, Mom, after your chemo, could you take me and my friend to the movies?' Well, I was so appalled that she would think… and then I said to myself, 'Wait a second, she thinks it's no big deal. She's not worrying that I'm going to die. She wants to go to the movies with her friend. This is a normal teenager thing. Let's be thankful,' " Val says, laughing again, "I told her, 'Of course I'm not taking you to the movies, nice try Maddy, but thanks for asking.' "

Michael excuses himself to get a glass of water. While he is filling his glass with ice, Val confides, "Michael went to every chemo treatment with me, every single appointment. That was just how it went." As he sits back down Val looks over at him thoughtfully. "And positive people who were around me would talk to me and have faith in me," she continues, "and I figured if they thought I could do this, then I could do this. There was courage and there was hope. And there were times that didn't feel very courageous or hopeful. But then a friend would say something like, 'It is what it is Val. Worry about what you can worry about and change it.' "

"I remember when I was sitting on the gurney in the hospital waiting for the node dissection," she explains. "They had to put the dye in for the node dissection, and they wanted me to move the dye around, kind of manually massage it, to make sure that it got where it needed to." She makes the motions with her hands. "I remember lying there out in the hall. I didn't care who walked by the

pauses to gather her emotions. Taking the tissue she dabs her teary eyes one last time. "Before the breast cancer I wasn't a very public person," she admits, "but I heard today about a woman who is devastated, obviously, by her breast cancer diagnosis and she wants to crawl under a rock, maybe

"There was courage and there was hope. And there were times that didn't feel very courageous or hopeful."

gurney seeing me feel myself up while I was doing that, because I just wanted that dye to get where it needed to. To tell us what we needed to know so we could treat it properly. But I also had this feeling, like of being on other women's shoulders," she says raising her arms in the air. "Like maybe, I didn't have the courage myself, but these women were lifting me up and giving me the strength that I needed."

"It was an endurance test, that year," sighs Val, holding the crumpled tissue in her hand. "In addition to breast cancer, the dog died. We had to get a puppy because I wasn't going to have it be sad in the house. My father died. And then, my daughter Becca's Bat Mitzvah was March first, a year after the mastectomies. It was right after Shiva (the Jewish seven-day mourning period) for my father. So it was a pretty unbelievable year," Val says, dabbing more tears.

Reliving her journey, the impact of Val's experience has caught up with her, and she

go out of town and not tell her kids. But I don't think you can do those things." She hesitates, briefly, searching for the right words.

"I think you want to send a message to your kids that you are strong," she sits up confidently, "and that things come up in life that aren't planned, that aren't great. And you just have to take what you get and deal with it. Try to grab all the life you can out of things. So I think that if it becomes a shame or something to hide, that not only will you not have support from other people, but your family won't get that support. And I think that everyone in the family needs that emotional support because you can't do this endurance test alone."

Steven Copit, MD
Plastic Surgeon

Jefferson Plastic Surgery, where Dr. Steven Copit is a partner, is located, of all places, on the fifteenth floor of the Wills Eye Hospital Building in Philadelphia, PA. Looking out the window of this beautifully decorated office is a bird's-eye view of the surrounding city. On the north side you can gaze down upon the historic structure of the Walnut Street Theatre Company, the oldest theatre in America. The journey which brought Dr. Copit here, where he is recognized as one of the finest breast reconstruction surgeons in town, began when he was a young boy.

"I had known my senior partner, Jim Fox, since I was a kid," he says, switching the lights on to his dark office, "After I finished my two years of plastic surgery training at University of Texas Southwestern, my wife, Debbie, and I decided to move back to the Philadelphia area. We always knew we wanted to settle here. I came into this practice in 1995, and as the junior guy you wind up doing a lot of breast reconstruction." He looks up from shuffling a stack of papers on his desk. "You're the doctor who sees patients in the hospital in addition to trying to develop a cosmetic surgery practice and other things."

Upon his return to Philadelphia, Albert Einstein Medical Center invited Steve to work with their multi-disciplinary breast cancer program as well. "I had done a lot of breast reconstruction in my training so I jumped at

down into a chair. "It's true, cosmetic surgery does pay better and takes less time," he admits, "but I feel that balance is important for me. There are days when I'm working hard all day on a breast

"Breast reconstruction surgery is the most gratifying part of my practice."

the offer. Not only did I come back and immediately start dong a lot of reconstruction at Jefferson, but I started doing a lot of it at Einstein too." In a short time, Copit became the breast reconstruction surgeon for two of the three busiest breast cancer programs in Philadelphia, the third being University of Pennsylvania. "I think like anything else," he comments, "the more you do something, the better you get at it."

Dr. Copit walks across the hall to the conference room. On the rear wall hangs a large portrait of the practice's founding partner, Warren Davis. Like the rest of the offices here, it, too, is impeccably decorated with fine furniture. The walls are covered in faux leather wallpaper and beautiful artwork. With such a feeling of classy, sophistication, one has to wonder why any plastic surgeon would even choose to do breast reconstructions. The procedures themselves require many surgical hours and insurance reimbursements for them are exceedingly low. Cosmetic procedures like liposuction, on the other hand, take much less time and bring higher profit margins.

"I have friends who ask why I even bother with the reconstruction," says Copit, settling

reconstruction and my partner is doing liposuction and then going home early to be with his kids, and then I think," he shakes his head, a bit bewildered. "But I enjoy it. Although I love doing cosmetic surgery, breast reconstruction surgery is the most gratifying part of my practice, in terms of the emotional feedback I get from patients. I get more cards and baked goods from breast reconstruction patients than anybody else," he says warmly.

Breast reconstruction has been available for more than thirty years. In its early days, surgeons only used silicone implants. Now, numerous techniques have been developed using a woman's natural tissues rather than implants. Still, today both silicone and saline implants are available. The biggest change in reconstruction over the last twenty years, according to Copit, has been the evolution of the mastectomy.

Up until the early 1970s, surgeons performed radical mastectomies, but during that time the modified radical mastectomy was perfected. "Breast surgeons today have many more concerns for what they're doing, trying to cure patients without overly maiming them, and also having concern for what the mastectomy looks like. Twenty or thirty years ago breast surgeons never called plastic surgeons and said, 'She looks great' or 'Nice job, we did good today,' " he says running his fingers through his silver hair.

"When lumpectomies were first pioneered in the late 1970s, mastectomies were very disfiguring, reconstructions were poor, and really saving a shrunken, radiated breast was still better than having a mastectomy.

"Breast reconstruction has nothing to do with prognosis, it's about quality of life."

But as mastectomies have improved and we now see the late effects of radiation for lumpectomy, a lot of breast cancer patients are opting for reconstruction. I see patients everyday who say, 'Why would I have my breast get all shriveled up from radiation and keep a one percent chance per year of recurrence when I can have that,' " Dr. Copit points to a picture of a reconstructed breast he shows his patients. "And you know, for some women reconstruction can be better, not many, but for some it can definitely be more functional and even flattering. It can be a better size, it can be lifted, maybe the breast isn't droopy. Those are all extras that we never encourage or promise. But really as mastectomy has improved reconstruction has gotten a lot, lot better, even in just the past fifteen years. And it's all part of the journey."

While the overall incidence of breast reconstruction is low in the country, only

about 16 percent of women have it done at the time of mastectomy and only 10 to 15 percent of women have it done later. In urban regions, nearly 100 percent of women having mastectomy have reconstruction. "Most everyone around here having mastectomy gets evaluated by a plastic surgeon," explains Copit, "because we live in a very avante garde, very progressive medical area of the country. But out in the rest of the U.S., say a place like Montana, a lot of women are not offered breast reconstruction. It's just not available," he frowns.

This available procedure brings a steady flow of patients to Dr. Copit's office. "That first consultation is kind of devastating for the patient. My longest consults are with breast reconstruction patients. Probably the hardest part with breast reconstruction, in all of plastic surgery, maybe even all of surgery," he says twirling the cufflink in his left shirtsleeve, "is defining expectations, compressing the conversation to what is reasonable for them to expect in terms of post-op pain, post-op look, post-op anything," he adds.

"A lot of breast cancer patients come with families, so I work to corralling them into, 'This is what we can do. No, we can't do that. You can't have this, but you can have that,' " he motions with his hands. "There is no perfect breast reconstruction, only

different choices, and they each have their own pros and cons. The key is to line up the patient with their best choice. Each operation has certain upsides and certain downsides, none of them are perfect, and the art is to find the right one for each patient. That's the hard part. I'm a very accurate surgeon. I'm pretty good at hitting the mark, but I have to get everybody on the same page and to make sure they all understand. For me, the operations are the easiest part."

A self-described practical physician, Dr. Copit often transfers his practical ideals onto his patients. "Based on my experience very few women are happy with their breasts. Over

time they change shape, they become bigger or smaller, they can sag. And yet women say to me all the time, 'I can't believe I'm going to have to lose my breasts.' I do understand that there are emotional attachments to a breast. But literally a breast is nothing more than a mound of fat and fibrous tissue. And that is not, by any means said to minimize its importance to a woman nor to minimize that it's not a part of her. I tell my patients all the time, 'Breasts are an appendage. It's not your heart and it's not your soul.' "

Most breast cancer patients are so focused on just staying alive that they can't see beyond the here and now, and it's his job,

wear a prosthesis. They'll say to me, 'I don't care about that,' and I'll say, 'But you will. Next year, next summer when you're going to the shore and you can't wear a bathing suit, you will care a lot and we need to worry about that.' So I need to get my patients to think long term, to make a decision now about what their life will be like a year from now. This is the part that can be very challenging," he says, tapping his folded hands on the table.

"A lot of breast cancer patients think, 'I should just focus on having my cancer removed and not worry about what I'm going to look like.' Breast reconstruction has nothing to do with prognosis; it's about quality of life. No woman should punish herself by not having reconstruction. Martyring herself will not make her live for one more minute. Reconstruction has nothing to do with that, but that's what many women think."

"I had a patient say to me the other day, 'I want you to make me whole again.' You see, I disagree when people say breast reconstruction can make a woman feel whole again," he says, rubbing his eyebrows. "The reality is when the lights are on and the clothes come off, there are scars and incisions. There is absolutely no way around that. She won't feel whole and I think that comment makes a woman feel bad. She has every right not to feel whole. She has scars on her body." His voice softens gently.

says Copit, to get them to envision their life one year from their diagnosis. "I'll say to my patients, 'I know you just want to live, I understand that, and if I told you right now you could cut your right arm off because it would let you live you would let me do it now here in the office.' I tell them reconstruction has nothing to do with their living and dying. Their cancer prognosis has to do with lymph node status or whatever else their breast surgeon and oncologist says. My job is to talk about what they're going to do about next year," he says, waving his hand forward.

"Most patients can't imagine how inconvenient their life will be if they have to

"When she looks in the mirror she sees she is not the person she used to be, and she is mourning that. She is entitled to that emotion. I can't make a woman feel whole again, but what I strive to do is to make her feel and look normal. So for me the concept is to create a mound that functions well in clothing and bathing suits so that a woman can have her old life back. And that's essentially the goal of breast reconstruction: form, function, and fashion," Copit says.

"We live in a society where the female form is worshipped and the fact is women wear clothing that is designed so there is a space here," he says, placing his hands on his chest, "and my goal as the surgeon is to fill that space as best I can, so that my patient can get through a whole day without the reminder of what she went through five years ago. To get her to the point where she can wake up, take a shower, get dressed, and go about her business, where her only concerns are going to work or complaining that her husband's a pain or the kids are whining."

"Breast reconstruction has nothing to do with vanity and everything to do with being normal. It's also about convenience. The convenience to wear clothes and bathing suits, and to look normal wearing them. If I can make a shape and a figure that my patient feels good about, then that is all gravy," he smiles, smoothing out his tie.

"I spend a lot of time just talking with my patients and I tell them the only thing I can do is provide them with something that will make their life easier and better. Breast reconstruction is the most emotionally draining part of my job, but it is the most gratifying part of my practice. At the end of the day when I'm sitting at my desk dictating, I feel like I did something good for somebody today."

"I can't make a woman feel whole again, but what I strive to do is to make her feel and look normal."

Philla Barkhorn
Breast Cancer Survivor

The workmen outside Philla's home are swarming like bees on a hive. These busy workers of various trades are constructing Philla's new, spacious artist studio housed above the family's new three-car garage. Inside, the Barkhorn home is filled with a variety of artwork; oil paintings, sculptures, and portraits, a few of the pieces painted by Philla, herself, others by her paternal grandfather, Peter Helck, an American artist from the early twentieth century. Philla's journey to becoming a portrait artist bloomed during her breast cancer diagnosis.

Philla walks down the long hallway from her kitchen, past the family room where one of her sons is relaxing in front of the television on this hot summer morning. She comes to the enclosed porch in the back of her home, makes herself comfortable in a cushy loveseat, and recounts when she first learned she had breast cancer.

"I went for a routine mammogram in January 2006 and they found something and wanted me to come back. I didn't think anything of it at the time. So I went back and they definitely saw something they didn't like and that's when I realized something might possibly be wrong." The dim sound of the television can be heard from the den. "In a week, I had a core needle biopsy and was diagnosed with DCIS. I was told the cancer was curable so I knew in that one week that I was going to live," Philla sighs in relief. "But you know, going through it, your whole life flashes in front of your eyes and it makes you wonder." Philla spent that time reflecting on her three young children, Austin, Danny and Adelaide, and her husband, Jonathan.

As a social worker trained in group counseling, Philla knew the benefits of therapy and wasted no time at all putting herself into a breast cancer support group. "After I called my husband and best friend and told them the news, I went on the Internet and found a local group at Pathways in Summit, NJ, called and spoke with the director right away. In her series of questions she asked me when I was diagnosed and I said, 'Oh, about forty-five minutes ago.' Well she burst out laughing and said, 'That is a record!' I told her, 'I'm a social worker and I know what I need. And I need to be in a group immediately!' I was diagnosed February ninth and my first support group was Tuesday, February fourteenth."

Philla reaches for a glass of lemonade on the coffee table. "I went to this group, walked in, and there was Diana, Camille and then there was Lisa, small and quiet," she describes, holding her drink. "These were the three women who made the biggest impression on me. There were other women who came and went. At the time I was very focused on myself and I was very, very angry. I could not believe I had cancer after living such a healthy life."

Philla opted for a unilateral mastectomy with reconstruction instead of radiation therapy. While she was spared the pain of chemotherapy, she was surprised to have feelings other than relief and gratitude after her surgery. The breast cancer support group was the place where Philla could share and explore her feelings. "Over time I got to know these women. About a month after I began the support group, Lisa stopped coming to the sessions," her voice trembles slightly, "and I didn't understand why. The last time I saw her, she gave me a hug and she was so frail. It was the kind of thing where it was almost an air hug because I was afraid to hurt her. It just wasn't computing in my mind that she was dying. I didn't know," she shrugs her shoulders.

"The following week we were told Lisa wasn't coming to group anymore and we were told not to email her. We were all so surprised, asking why. The leaders told us Lisa was in the hospital and she was dying. I was just shocked. I asked if she had known she was dying and they said yes. One group leader said we should pray for her death and I just couldn't do that, I just couldn't," Philla shakes her head disconsolately, tears rolling down her cheeks.

"I was so angry because I wanted to pray for her to get well. She died, I believe, April fourth. I was just devastated. I had met her only three or four times, an hour each. But Lisa sent me emails, she sent me cards, she gave me advice. She was really an amazing person. In group she was gentle, listened well, but when she spoke I soaked it in. She touched me profoundly. When I heard she died, I kept saying, 'I have to paint her, I have to paint her,' " she whispers in a little girl's voice.

During this time, Philla had already decided to create a series of portraits of women whose lives had been touched by cancer. Dubbing it, "The Portrait Project," Philla began by painting a close-up portrait of her mother, Eileen Helck, an elegantly beautiful woman who passed away in 1993 from pancreatic cancer, and also a portrait of her niece, Nora Helck, whose mother had breast cancer. "At the time I was also working on a portrait of me and my daughter, Adelaide, but I was gripped with the need to memorialize Lisa," explains Philla. "So I asked the group leaders if I could have Lisa's contact information so I could get her photograph."

In the meantime, Philla kept busy with her portraits and art classes at the NJ Center for Visual Arts. In August 2007, she received an email from Pathways, her cancer support group, inviting cancer survivors to participate in an art show they were hosting that October. "Any survivor was invited to submit poetry, sculpture, paintings, whatever," Philla explains excitedly, "but it had to do something with cancer. I had finished the portrait of me and of my niece, so I thought, 'Oh, what the heck.' It solidified even more, my idea to do the portrait series of women."

After nearly ten months, Philla finally received word from Lisa's family and they supplied Philla with the photograph she needed to create the portrait. "It was this tiny little snapshot of Lisa and her mother, Marie," Philla says, forming a little square with her hands. "I took the photo to the camera store, had it blown up, color copied, the whole thing."

When she first began the portrait it was springtime 2007 and she was still enrolled in art classes, but as the portrait developed, so did Philla's confidence as an artist. She

Above, Philla with the portrait of her mother, Eileen Helck. Eileen died of pancreatic cancer in 1993. Left, photograph of the portrait of Lisa from Philla's support group, along with the note from Lisa's mother, Marie.

decided to go into business and set up a basement studio in her home. "Working on this portrait in my basement studio, I really let loose," Philla says. "It felt like I was communicating with Lisa. Now, I'm an atheist," she admits, leaning forward in her

seat. "I would like to believe that God exists. I would like to believe that heaven exists. I'm open to the possibility. But really and truly, I'm an atheist." She sits back in her seat. "So, I painted Lisa's portrait and as I was doing so, I talked to her. I cried. I ranted. I raved. But it was her smiling face looking back at me. I felt completely connected to her." Philla takes the back of her hand and wipes away some tears staining her cheeks.

Philla steps inside for a moment and returns carrying a box of tissues. "I had a lot of

Philla with the portrait of herself with her daughter, Adelaide. Adelaide is now eight years old.

"I read that note and thought to myself, 'Oh my God.' So something magical was going on when I did Lisa's painting. It was very good for me, very cathartic, because I have a lot of feelings about having breast cancer. But I don't feel like I'm entitled to my feelings because I'm alive. And it's always been very hard for me to talk about it. I can't stand it when people feel sorry for me, because really I am so blessed. All right I'm an atheist, but I'm very blessed," she chuckles seriously.

The newest portrait Philla is working on is of her sister-in-law, Tempe and her husband, Peter, Philla's brother. Tempe is Nora Helck's mother, and Tempe died from breast cancer in 2007. "I'd known and idolized Tempe all my life. She was the funniest and most creative person you'd ever want to meet," reflects Philla.

In 1998, Tempe was diagnosed with Stage IV breast cancer. "There was no surgery to be done," Philla says quietly. "It was so advanced the doctors said they would give her as much time as they can. And they gave her almost eight years, which is unbelievable," she says dabbing her tears. She sniffles a little. "Tempe gave me perspective. When I was diagnosed and knew my cancer was not terminal, I said to myself, 'You know what Philla, you need to live your life fully because there are other people who can't.' "

In addition to her painting, Philla is actively involved in the Danskin Women's Triathlon, participating every year since 2005. After finishing her first race she became inspired to create a group from Chatham Township, the

emotions drawing my mother but there was something with Lisa, hers was the most intimate," she says, waving a tissue in the air. "Her mom wrote me a letter after she received the portrait and it really rings true what she wrote." Philla opens the note card her voice quivering as she reads, 'It was like having my daughter back. I have prayed since Lisa's death that I would receive a sign that she was at peace. On Saturday, looking at her serene, peaceful face, I knew God had answered my prayers.' "

65

"I think getting cancer is definitely a wake-up call. It makes you think about how many days you have left on this planet and what you are going to do with them."

NJ suburb where she lives. With the help of a few other tri-athletes, Philla organized and promoted Triwomen, the Chatham group, which provides participants with training workshops and social gatherings. But it is Philla's work as a portrait artist that allows her to do something which is very meaningful to herself and to other people.

"Memorializing someone in a portrait means so much to the family. This is what resonates most with me. As a social worker you're trained to always want to help people. You can't bring back someone who has died, but you can show people that you care when they are faced with such a loss. That was what Lisa's mother, Marie, was so struck by. That someone would care enough to do this for her. When my mom was sick," Philla soberly remembers, "I was much younger, I was about thirty. And people would say to me, 'I'll pray for you, I'll pray for your mother, or your mother's in my prayers.' And again, I wasn't one who prayed," she says, putting her hand to her chest, "but I thought, it matters that someone wants to pray for me, and that's what gave me any kind of comfort, knowing that people cared."

"I've worked a lot with people who were truly suffering," Philla says, referring to her days as a social worker, "and that's where I feel my best talent lies, helping people. I think getting cancer is definitely a wake-up call. It makes you think about how many days you have left on this planet and what you are going to do with them. It definitely made me wonder, 'Why I am here? What is my purpose in life?' Being a portrait artist gives me an incredibly good feeling, but it also allows me to offer some kind of assistance to those who are hurting from illness or loss."

Page 61, Philla with the portrait of her sister-in-law Tempe and husband, Peter, Philla's brother. Tempe died of metastatic breast cancer in 2007.

Michele Rossi, LCSW
Support Group Facilitator

The long narrow driveway leading to the entrance of The Wellness Community in Wilmington, DE is covered with a fresh layer of soft, powdered snow. The eighteenth century converted house and the beautiful property it sits on shimmers and glistens as the morning sun rises in the sky. It is a tranquil and equally breathtaking setting and the perfect location for an organization dedicated to helping and healing people with cancer.

Michele Rossi, a clinical staff member, strolls inside, dressed casually in sweats and a sweatshirt, her hair pulled up in a high ponytail. It's her day off, but Michele has willingly ventured in to share her journey as the center's group facilitator for Friends on the Mend, a breast cancer support group. The Wellness Community is a national, non-profit organization providing cancer support services to patients and their loved ones. All programs, which are professionally facilitated, are free and focus on handling the emotional aspects of the disease. The Wilmington affiliate opened in 1996.

Michele takes a seat on a cushy leather sofa in the main meeting room. "Well I have an interesting story," she laughs boldly, "because I started out in broadcasting. I got tired of being the conduit of information and decided I wanted to be the direct reason for good things to happen. So while I was a PR director at a school I went back to college at Widener University in Philadelphia, PA, in the evenings for social work." Rossi began her new career doing one on one therapy and support therapy, working with divorce and

separation, and kids with a variety of special needs. "I really was interested in medical social work. I wanted to work in pediatric oncology but I couldn't get in, it's a tight field. So I ended up working at a place called Cancer Care Connection."

In the beginning of her social work schooling, Michele met Sean Hebbel, the program director at Wellness. "I tried desperately to be an intern here but they were looking for licensed people but I wasn't licensed yet, so I kept in touch with Sean. He called me when The Wellness Community wanted to do a children's group. I started here around 1998 or so, working only with kids groups, not kids with cancer," she clarifies, "but children who had someone significant in their lives, usually their parents, who had cancer." Besides Sean Hebbel, Michele is the longest running facilitator at The Wellness Community.

"Shoot years ahead," Rossi says, waving her right hand forward, "and I'm working at the Helen Graham Cancer Center in Wilmington. Not to be morbid, but at Helen Graham, they divided our work by body parts. I was assigned to breast cancer and most of the other women's cancers, also prostate, bladder, and kidney cancers. But breast cancer was by far the biggest group I worked with. I had to learn intensively about breast cancer. Then we started running breast cancer support groups there. Sometime in 2003, Sean asked me to run a ten week Return to Wellness Program, which is something the national Wellness Community had been running."

The program was specifically for breast cancer patients, and participants in the program had to be six months out of treatment. Participants came to The Wellness Community once a week, where they were divided into two groups. In the first hour, one group did yoga while the other group did strength training. After five weeks they switched exercise programs. But the second hour was always spent together in a support group led by Rossi. Another night a week all participants went to Christiana Hospital in Wilmington where they attended presentations by doctors and nutritionists.

"It was a very nice program," recalls Rossi. "And when the ten weeks ended the group wanted to stay together and asked if I would keep it running. Friends on the Mend has been going ever since. We'll be starting our

when support groups really started to take off with the baby boomer generation. "They're more open to support groups and the support group format than previous generations were," comments Rossi.

The biggest benefit of how support groups function today is the role of the professional facilitator. "A group facilitator is absolutely different than being a group therapist," explains Rossi. "And it's hard, you really have to sit on your hands sometimes. But my role is to facilitate conversation within the group. We have all personality types in the group. If someone is maybe dominating the conversation and I sense that people are uncomfortable with that, I might have to say, 'Oh, I'm wondering what Mary thinks about this,' or, 'Sue, you've been quiet for awhile, what do you think about this?' "

"A support group is a safe place to talk about things, but the point of the group is to not always talk about cancer."

eighth year this April," she smiles happily. While the core group is made up of ten women, Rossi says they would gladly welcome men who have had breast cancer.

About thirty years ago, according to Sean Hebbel, organizations like the American Cancer Society would run support groups which were usually hospital based. If they were community based, they were usually inside churches. Most were self-help and self-facilitated. It wasn't until the late 1970s

"We have one woman who almost never speaks, but when she does it's like God is talking," Rossi says, turning her head upwards towards heaven. "We all stop when she speaks because we know something profound is going to come out of her mouth. I'm really judging all of the time. They're not all extroverts and part of my role is to gage, take a temperature on the group and keep things going smooth. A facilitator is really like a referee. Our job is to keep everybody safe."

Most importantly, says Rossi, a support group is a place where people who share a common bond can come together and feel safe to talk about things. "Everybody in the room shares the same experience. I think people need to understand a support group is not about being picked apart and it's not about having your life analyzed. It's simply a group of people that have had a trauma in their life. I really try to emphasize that having cancer is a trauma. I don't care if someone had DCIS or inflammatory breast cancer; cancer is a trauma that carries a stigma in this society as well. But it's life threatening and the first thing someone thinks about is, 'Am I going to die?' So group members all share that experience of having their mortality shoved in their faces."

Unlike other group facilitators at The Wellness Community, Rossi runs things a bit differently in her support groups. After the usual introductions and chit chat, Rossi always checks in with everybody. "I always ask who had scans since the last time and when are scans coming up," she says. "There is one member who is designated to disseminate information about another member. We have an Internet chain and a phone chain because we want to know how someone did."

"This group is very active about keeping in touch via phone and e-mail. You know what's interesting, especially about a long-time group, is it's not always cancer we talk about. A support group is a safe place to talk about things, but the point of the group is to not always talk about cancer. These women become attached to one another and become interested in each other's lives. It often goes beyond the cancer, especially when no one in the group has a pressing issue. We want to know how their kid did on a test or how their husband made out with work."

Friends on the Mend members feel so comfortable with each other that they often boss each other around a little, says Rossi. 'They'll say to each other, 'What do you mean you haven't scheduled your mammogram? Get with the program!' " she explains, her hands motioning as she speaks. "So they hold each other accountable. Or maybe someone can't say anything more at home like, 'I have pain in my hip and I'm really scared,' because they'll get poo-poo'd by their family. But in support group we'll say, 'You have a pain in your hip, wow that's really scary, what are you going to do about it?' It's always about how we can support someone's concern."

The other really great advantage about a support group, Rossi says, is the valuable exchange of information on medicines and their side effects, alternative medicines, and alternative therapy places. "Someone might say 'Oh, this worked for me you should try this,' " explains Rossi. "Do you know we have had people in group that have had a swollen arm and have no idea they have had lymphedema. And when we tell them, they say, 'I have what?' They just didn't know. So they then knew they needed to take care of it."

At a recent meeting Michele asked her breast cancer support group how they're doing with their wills, advance directives, and life insurance. "Periodically, I will bring it up on purpose, especially when everyone is doing so well. I try to tell people, 'Don't wait until you're on your deathbed, have these conversations with your family now. Get this stuff taken care of because the people in your life are going to be devastated at that time. Give them the gift of having it done.' "

Michele is jovial, direct, and to the point in a very caring manner. Her spirited personality always projects an upbeat tone. Yet she is the first to say that one advantage of a support group is that it is a place where you don't always have to be positive. "I think many patients feel obligated to stay 'up' and 'positive' for others, especially their partners and family," she explains, readjusting her ponytail. "It can be overwhelming and it's not realistic. As humans we can feel many things at once; hope and despair. Feelings come and go in cycles or waves. This is the normal rhythm of life," she says caringly. "I think this is so important for people to discuss and understand."

Of all the things about Friends on the Mend, Rossi is touched most by the camaraderie and closeness of the participants. "People need to know we laugh a lot here. It's not just doom and gloom," she says. "Almost everyone here at Wellness has a way we end the group session which is usually standing in a circle, either holding hands or holding each other by around the back. We talk about how much the group meant or to think about somebody who was not here or who may be hurting. It's the caring that these women show each other and me." Her voice softens.

"We get choked up here a lot. I do," she nods slightly, "especially at the end when we're all here holding each other. They'll say to each other, 'I love you. I don't know what I'd do without this group. Thank God this group is here.' This is a very huggy kind of place, a very affectionate place. I'll often leave here happy and sniffling."

"People need to know we laugh a lot here. It's not just doom and gloom."

Norma E. Roth
Breast Cancer Survivor

My pink ribbon journey started long before my breast cancer diagnosis. Long before the pink ribbon became the symbol for breast cancer awareness. My journey goes back three generations. It is the voice of one but the story of many.

I was born in 1963, the youngest of four girls. There are only four and a half years between my oldest sister, Marsha, and me. To say the least, my parents had their hands full with four young children. But that didn't stop them from packing us into the car nearly every Sunday afternoon for a visit with my grandparents in Brooklyn, NY.

When we pulled up to the apartment building on Ocean Parkway where my mom grew up, my sisters and I would scramble out of the car and race through the lobby to the elevator, where we would then elbow each other out of the way in our attempt to press the elevator button first. We each took a turn pressing the button repeatedly, something that drove my parents crazy. Grandma Yetta greeted us at the door while Grandpa Benny sat in his recliner in the bedroom, listening to his transistor radio close to his ear.

It was here in Apt. 5H, a cozy place, where my sisters and I would often overhear the hushed conversations about the "Sosne Curse." While my sisters and I played, the adults whispered about Grandpa's sister, Dora, who died from breast cancer at age fifty-three and his other sister, Sarah, who lived two floors below my grandparents. Aunt Sarah was adored for her witty sense of

humor, and most notably, her scrumptious, homemade rugalach. Aunt Sarah had breast cancer too, but she was considered lucky. The cancer took her breast, but it didn't take her life. They would also talk about Grandma Yetta's sister, my Aunt Sarah Leit. She too had breast cancer. I never met Aunt Dora; breast cancer claimed her life before I was born. Grandma Yetta also had breast cancer in her early forties but she kept it a huge secret from most everyone. She never, ever once spoke of it to us during her life. My sisters and I only learned about it years after her death.

To complicate my developing mind even more, Aunt Natalie, who was married to my father's brother, died from breast cancer in 1966. I was only three years old when she died, but at that tender age, I had more relatives dead or afflicted from breast cancer than most people, in that era, had known in a lifetime.

As we grew into young adults, my mother spoke more openly to me and my sisters about the "Sosne Curse" and how she always anticipated the next shoe to fall. In February 1988, a few months after my engagement to my husband, Joel, it became obvious my mother was not herself. She had always been boisterous, opinionated, and never at a loss for words. But now she was unusually quiet and became secretive about where she was going or where she had been. One day, while she sat in her usual corner seat on the living room sofa, she made an announcement. "Listen up clearly because I'm only going to say this once." Her voice was nervous and shaky with her thick Brooklyn accent. "Last week I went to a doctor because I felt a lump in my breast. He did a needle aspiration for a biopsy. It turns out, I have breast cancer." She was fifty-five years old. The shoe had finally fallen, loud and hard.

My mother had Stage III breast cancer which the oncologist described as aggressive and fast growing. When I was growing up my mother used to say, "Behind every gray cloud is a silver lining." Despite the grim news, somehow she considered herself

first cousin. Bea's mother, Sarah, and my mother's father, Benny, were siblings. Bea and my mother grew up together in the same apartment building in Brooklyn, adored each other, and were extremely close. The news of Bea's cancer rocked my mother to her core. Cancer preyed on everyone dear to her heart. Bea died in 1991 and my mother mourned the loss until her own death years later.

In July 1992, I made my mother the proud grandma of a beautiful baby girl, Shayna Rose. The summer of 1993, after months of suffering

"I took all of my films and met with Dr. Somers, my breast surgeon... Dr. Somers insisted on a biopsy, based solely on my alarming family history."

lucky. "My Aunt Dora was already dead at age fifty-three," she told us frankly. In her mind, she was ahead of the game by two years. She had a unilateral mastectomy followed by six months of chemotherapy. After chemotherapy, the oncologist put her on a drug called, Tamoxifen, which was proven to slow the growth of cancer cells in estrogen positive breast cancer. He was hopeful it would benefit my mother and she took it for five years.

Sometime in 1990, my mother called me sounding very distressed. "What's wrong, did someone die?" I asked fearing something dreadful. "Bea has ovarian cancer," she said, her voice cracking. Bea was my mother's

a chronic cough, she learned her cancer metastasized to her windpipe. "Those fucking cancer cells are back," she told us bluntly. This time, she had radiation and chemotherapy. Despite all the medicines, her cancer continued to metastasize during the next year. She needed a port for the chemotherapy because all of her good veins had collapsed. She suffered greatly.

In August 1994, she was gravely ill and hospitalized for a blood infection while my father prayed daily for the cancer to stop spreading. Dr. Mark Brower, her oncologist, used every resource available to treat her cancer. Although she did not meet the criteria, he even tried to get her into a Taxol

75

drug study. In 1994, Taxol was an experimental chemotherapy drug and in clinical research trials was showing promising early results in fighting breast cancers. As she lay in her hospital bed, Dr. Brower approached my mother about the possibility of her taking this drug. She put up her hands in protest. "Enough is enough," she said firmly to my tearful father standing at her bedside. My mother died August 16, 1994, one week before her sixty-first birthday. The days grew dark and solemn after her death.

In June 1995, my son Jeremy was born spreading sunshine back into our lives. Sometime in late August while we were all out for dinner celebrating mine and my sister Sharon's birthdays, my father put down his menu and said, "Well, girls, I have some bad news." My sisters and I looked from one to another, thinking what could possibly be wrong now. "Your Auntie Rochelle has breast cancer," he said wearily.

Aunt Rochelle was my mother's younger sister. Our jaws dropped in utter shock and disbelief. It was only a year since my mother's death and that horrible "Sosne Curse" had struck again. My father was visibly distraught as he explained Aunt Rochelle had Stage I cancer, would have a lumpectomy with chemotherapy and radiation. She was expected to make a full recovery, he said, offering us a forced smile. Today, Aunt Rochelle is the longest breast cancer survivor in the Sosne family and for this she deserves a pink ribbon medal!

In 1997, I jumped at an opportunity to participate in a BRCA1/2 gene study for

Henrietta (Yetta) Leit Sosne with her two daughters, Marlene (left) and Rochelle (right)

Ashkenazi Jews coordinated by Cooper University Hospital in Camden, NJ. There was a BRCA mutation in the Sosne family which we were confident was responsible for the breast and ovarian cancer that plagued our relatives, and I wanted to know if I was a carrier. My sisters refused to participate and pestered me about being tested. "I want to know," I explained, to which they always asked belligerently, "But why would you want to know that?" I wanted to know for my own peace of mind and felt the information would help guide my future medical care. After several counseling sessions and many large vials of blood later, I learned I was not a carrier of any BRCA1/2 mutation. While this did not exclude me from ever getting breast cancer, the relief was enormous.

In 1998, I had my third child, Marlena, named for my mother, Marlene. Their birthdays are just one day apart and they share the same brown eyes, speckled with flecks of yellow light. Although I didn't have a BRCA mutation and felt certain I would never get breast cancer, I remained proactive about my breast health and had my first mammogram at age thirty-six.

In January 2004, I went for my annual mammogram, albeit three months late. I blamed the tardiness on my now forty year-old mind. Like in years past, I left the imaging center and never gave the mammogram another thought, until five days later when my telephone rang.

"Since you won't tell me what's going on, you can fax over the pathology report to my primary care physician no later than 5:00 today. This way he can tell me what's wrong." I gave her the telephone number and she did what I asked.

Later that evening Dr. Hanley called. "Well, did they find something?" I asked. Dr. Hanley read the pathology report to me line by line. The radiologist found a small, non-palpable tumor in my right breast. The tumor he was describing sounded eerily familiar, just like my mother's. Same breast, same location within the breast. That's when sheer panic set in.

I had three children under the age of twelve, this could not be happening. My mind swirled with all kinds of unpleasant thoughts

"'Those are a lot of names there,' he commented, pointing to my chart with the seven names of all my relatives with breast or ovarian cancer."

"You need to come in right away for some follow-up X-rays of your right breast," said the very pleasant woman from Jefferson Breast Imaging in Philadelphia, PA. "Well what's wrong with my right breast that I need to come in immediately? Did they find something?" I asked her tersely. I badgered this poor woman but she offered only generic responses, none of which satisfied my panicking mind. "Here's what we're going to do," I said in an obnoxious tone.

as a sickening feeling swelled in my stomach. My dear doctor, sensing my hysteria, tried to calm and reassure me by saying, "Remember Norma, most breast tumors are benign," to which I politely replied, "Not in my family!" He reiterated several times, I needed a top-notch breast surgeon, and also told me not to worry until there was something to worry about. I appreciated his caring advice, and I tried, I really did, not to worry, but it's difficult to do when your mother is dead from breast cancer.

The next week I returned to Jefferson and they took magnified images of my right breast. "You see these," the radiologist said pointing to calcifications within the tumor. "These appear benign. But these few over here, it's hard to say. I think you should have a biopsy just to make certain," she said, patting my shoulder. I took all of my films and met with Dr. Somers, my breast surgeon. While he and the radiologist both felt the tumor was benign, Dr. Somers insisted on a biopsy, based solely on my alarming family history. "Those are a lot of names there," he commented, pointing to my chart with the seven names of all my relatives with breast or ovarian cancer.

I had a needle core biopsy on a Friday morning. "No matter what it turns out to be, you're going to be fine," Dr. Somers said afterwards, hugging and reassuring me.

He told me he would call late Tuesday afternoon with the pathology results. Instead, he called me early Tuesday morning. Of course, I was too busy getting my kids off to school to pick up my ringing house and cell phones. When I got the messages that he was trying to reach me, I knew it was not going to be a good day. When your doctor says, "You have cancer," those three words rip through your gut and change your life forever.

I had Ductal Carcinoma In Situ (DCIS), said Dr. Somers. "Not that there's any kind of good cancer, but DCIS is a good one to have," he said. "It's highly curable." He kept saying he was sorry during our conversation. I think he was more devastated than I was. "You have nothing to apologize for," I told him, "I knew all along in my heart I had cancer, even if you didn't."

Later that evening, Joel and I met with Dr. Somers, who meticulously explained to us the diagnosis and all of the treatment options. It turns out DCIS is 99 percent curable with a lumpectomy and six weeks of radiation. We came home somewhat relieved. I could be cured. Still, I went to bed feeling it truly sucked having breast cancer.

The next day Joel and my sister Debbie began calling family and friends. I saved my strength for "the talk" with my children and father. Remarkably, no one had a nervous breakdown, except maybe me. But regrettably, when Debbie spoke with Aunt Rochelle she learned some upsetting news. In the past six months two of our Sosne relatives had been diagnosed with breast cancer. The Sosne Curse was spreading like wildfire. There were now seven women, spanning three generations, stricken with breast cancer! (This number does not include Grandma Yetta and her sister Sarah from the other side of my family tree.)

At my father's urging I met with Dr. Brower. He is a nationally recognized oncologist/hematologist and my father trusted his medical advice implicitly. After reviewing my pathology slides and mammogram X-rays, Dr. Brower sat down at his desk. "So what do you think," I asked anxiously. "I think you're a very lucky woman," he replied. "Well I don't feel very lucky, why do you say that?" I asked impatiently. "Because whoever read your initial mammogram saved your life," he said.

Dr. Brower walked me and my father over to the illuminated X-rays. He pointed to the tumor with his finger. "This tumor is so small it blends in very well with the rest of your breast tissue," he commented. "The normal human eye would never notice it. But you see these?" he asked. My father and I squinted, not sure what he was referring to. Dr. Brower was pointing to the very teeny, tiny calcifications. We could barely see them amongst the breast tissue. "Only a highly trained person who reads a lot of mammograms would have noticed these calcification spots. They're too small. It took someone with a very skilled eye to detect them. I know you don't feel lucky right now, but you are, and I think when you're ready you should thank the radiologist. It's truly remarkable," he said, shaking his head in awe. That radiologist was none other than Dr. Catherine Piccoli.

After meeting with Dr. Brower, Joel and I discussed all of my options. I was seriously considering having the lumpectomy and radiation treatment. He thought I was crazy. "You're out of your mind," he said, shaking his head furiously, "With your family history you should just take the damn breasts off." I explained calmly, I wasn't quite ready to have them removed. Joel began sobbing uncontrollably, "We already had to bury your mother, don't make us bury you too," he pleaded through his tears.

After Joel's tearful plea, I decided to do some further research and spoke with other women who had DCIS and had mastectomy. I also read information about it on the Internet. Coincidentally, a week after my diagnosis, National Public Radio featured a story on the results of a nationwide study of women with DCIS. The study reported women with high-grade DCIS (like mine) who also had a family history of breast cancer (i.e. a mother or a sister) and had a lumpectomy with six weeks of radiation, usually developed an invasive cancer within three to five years. That study helped solidify my decision.

So while I didn't really want to part with my breasts, I was definitely not prepared to part from my children. If things turned out badly, Joel could always find another wife, I thought to myself, but my children could never have another mother. It was their three beautiful,

outcomes would be different. But Aunt Dora, Aunt Sarah Leit, and even Aunt Natalie really didn't have a chance for survival. Before the 1960s there was no chemotherapy. The only way to treat breast cancer was to remove it with a radical mastectomy. If the cancer grew back, the doctor simply cut it out where it had spread to, eventually leaving the woman with a butchered upper body.

In the early 1960s nitrogen mustard and a few other medicines were used to fight cancer. Then CMF (Cytoxan, Methotrexate and 5fu) was developed, and according to

"I think you're a very lucky woman...whoever read your initial mammogram saved your life."

sweet faces, peering back at me in my rearview mirror, which strongly influenced my decision to choose the most radical procedure for the most curable breast cancer.

On Monday, May 10, 2004, I had bilateral mastectomies with immediate breast reconstruction. It was the best decision and it saved my life. The pathology of my right breast noted one quadrant diseased with microscopic, high-grade DCIS and LCIS (lobular in situ cancer). Had I chosen to leave the breast in tact, the DCIS and LCIS would have grown into a lethal cancer within a few years.

As I look at my family tree and see the names of so many relatives who lost their lives to breast cancer, I am overcome with an indescribable sadness. If they were here today and had breast cancer surely their

Dr. Grana, everyone who had breast cancer got CMF. Eventually, Adriamycin got added to the mix. But only in the past twenty-five years, says Dr. Grana, has a whole array of drugs, including new chemotherapies like Taxol and hormone and biologic therapies been developed to fight breast cancer. These new drugs and advances in diagnostic tools, like digital mammography, ultrasound, and MRI, are responsible for the dramatic increases in breast cancer survival rates.

I owe my life to a mammogram and the comprehensive skills of radiologist/woman's breast imager, Catherine Piccoli. I am also alive today because I had a mastectomy instead of a lumpectomy. Although I was initially reluctant to have breast reconstruction, I'm really happy I did. As Dr. Copit says, "Breast reconstruction has nothing to do with vanity and everything to do with

being normal." Looking at me, you would never know I had bilateral mastectomies, thanks to my reconstruction. It's true, when the lights are on and the clothes come off I have scars and incisions, but I really don't care. I'm just grateful I'm alive to look at these scars everyday in the mirror.

I agree strongly with Dr. Somers when he says, "If you're afraid there might be cancer, if it's there, don't you think you better find it?" Absolutely! No one should fear breast cancer; when detected early, it's highly treatable. My mother was, intelligent, educated, and cultured, yet when it came to breast cancer she stuck her head in the sand. She was paralyzed with fear and became complacent about her breast health, despite her strong family history. When she felt the lump in her breast she foolishly walked around with it for awhile instead of immediately going to a doctor. My sisters and I often wonder, "Would Mom be alive today if she had just gone to the doctor right away?" We will never know the answer to that question. But one thing is certain; cancer, even the suspicion of cancer, requires immediate medical attention. Waiting only allows it to grow bigger, and when it comes to cancer, bigger is never better!

After my recovery, my sisters finally conceded and underwent genetic testing. One of my sisters tested positive for the BRCA mutation in the Sosne family. A month later she had her ovaries removed. By doing this she greatly reduced her risk for ovarian and breast cancer and remains cancer-free to this day. As Beth Peshkin points out, genetic testing is beneficial and can help guide you in making informed medical decisions, decisions that can save your life.

As my daughters become young women, I will heed Faye Feldman's advice and they will learn how to do a monthly breast self-exam, whether they like it or not. This simple step takes less than five minutes and could save their lives. I will do everything in my power to make sure they never, ever have to go through what I, my mother, grandmother, and all of my aunts and cousins endured with this disease.

When I think back six years ago, I still shake my head in disbelief that I had breast cancer. It was such a difficult time. Like Maria Matos, I look at the glass as half full. When Joel and I told our children I had breast cancer, they were understandably upset –after all, they associated breast cancer with the death of their grandmother. So I made sure to always project a positive attitude about it when I was with them.

Val Yasner is right when she says, "You can't do this endurance test alone." Like her and Michael, my family was surrounded with a loving support group of family and friends. My Hadassah friends provided my kids with school lunches and our family with home-cooked dinners every single day during my six-week recovery. Other friends came over and did housework or errands or just sat by my bed offering words of encouragement. We could not have healed without them. I would encourage someone with breast cancer to join a breast cancer support group. As Michele Rossi reminds us, "A support group is a safe place to talk about things."

My mother is dead now almost sixteen years. I can still hear her calling my name but each year her voice becomes fainter. Like Traci-Ann Delisser I often ask myself, "Did she really know how much I loved her?" I hope so. My mother's death taught me, like Beth Manusov said of her own cancer, not to get caught up in the minutia of life. There are many more important things to get upset about. Like James Grupenhoff, Joel and I relish any opportunity to share with Shayna, Jeremy and Marlena the wisdom of their Grandma Marlene, a bright star in the lives of many. And like Philla Barkhorn, even though I had breast cancer, I consider myself very fortunate. I never had to suffer through the ill effects of chemotherapy or radiation treatments.

I am truly blessed. It's true; behind every gray cloud there is a silver lining. Unlike my mother, I am cured.

"I am truly blessed. It's true; behind every gray cloud there is a silver lining. Unlike my mother, I am cured."

*"My pink ribbon journey started long before
my breast cancer diagnosis...
My journey goes back three generations.
It is the voice of one but the story of many."*

The Sosne Family

This photo represents the first generation of Sosne women with documented cases of breast cancer.

Here is my Grandpa Benny (bottom row, second from left) with his siblings and their respective spouses.
Aunt Dora (bottom row, first from left) died from metastatic breast cancer at age 53.
Aunt Sarah Sosne Koenig (bottom row, second from right) had breast cancer at age 65, she died in 1986, at age 76.
Grandma Yetta (nee Leit) is standing in the top row looking over Grandpa's shoulders.
She is a Sosne through marriage and she also had breast cancer in her 40's.

This pink ribbon represents Sarah Leit. She was my great aunt and
Grandma Yetta Leit Sosne's sister. Sarah died at age 58, in 1968, from cancer.
Unfortunately, there was no photo available of Sarah to include on this page.

The second generation...breast and ovarian cancer

Devoted sisters, Rochelle Sosne Glaser (left) and Marlene Sosne Roth (right), strike a pose in 1990.
My mother, Marlene, was diagnosed with breast cancer in 1988.
She died in 1994, at age 60, from metastatic breast cancer.
My Aunt Rochelle was diagnosed with breast cancer in 1995.
She continues to be breast cancer free.

Bea Koenig Libowsky was Marlene and Rochelle's first cousin. Bea's mother, Sarah Sosne Koenig, had breast cancer. Bea was diagnosed with ovarian cancer at age 58. Ovarian cancer took her life at age 59, in 1991.

The third generation

Devoted sisters, me (left) with my sister, Sharon Roth-Lichtenfeld, (right) striking a pose in 2005. Although I am BRCA mutation negative, I had DCIS and LCIS in 2004. Sharon is BRCA mutation positive. Never having had breast or ovarian cancer, she underwent prophylactic oophorectomy, in 2005 in a preemptive strike. Sharon remains breast and ovarian cancer free to this day.

Gail Libowsky Kazin is Bea Koenig Libowsky's daughter, and Sarah Sosne Koenig's granddaughter. Although Gail is BRCA mutation negative, she was diagnosed with invasive breast cancer in 2003. Gail, a nurse practitioner, is now cancer free, and is grateful for the time she has with her husband, Jerry, and their three sons, Ari, Zachary, and Isaac.

Natalie and Robert Roth surrounded by their four daughters, (from left to right) Rona, Bobbie, Lois, and Cheryl. (Circa late 1950's) Aunt Natalie was married to Robert, my father's brother. She was diagnosed with breast cancer at age 37. She died in 1966, at age 43, from metastatic breast cancer when I was just 3 years old. My mother, Marlene, said of Natalie, "I loved her like she was my own sister."

To Brandon, Shayna, and Carly,

Although we didn't get to know one another that well, I hope my legacy to you is one of faith, strength and character. You're the source of much joy. And I hope your mommies ever remind you of Grandma Marlene. I love you dearly. I'll try to walk beside you and lead you in the right path.

Marlene Sosne Roth dictated this note for her three grandchildren to her daughter, Debbie, about three days before she died. On her request, the Rabbi read this note, along with several others Marlene had dictated to her family, at her funeral. This note, just five sentences in length, has left a profound impact on all of her grandchildren. Her granddaughter Shayna, now 18, continues to keep this note close to her side.

Marlene Sosne Roth with her three grandchildren.

Marlene with Brandon Stein
(Sharon's son) in 1990

Marlene with Shayna Penn
(Norma's daughter) in 1993

Marlene with Carly Stein
(Sharon's daughter) in 1993

Where They Are Now

Maria Matos (Interview September 2007) – No personal update provided.

Catherine W. Piccoli, MD (Interview January 2007) – Dr.Piccoli continues her role as head of Women's Imaging at South Jersey Radiology. Now an empty-nester, she has time to revive favorite hobbies and sports including sewing costumes for her daughter, a budding actress at NYU, sailing the Chesapeake in her 1961 30' Hinckley sloop and club racing on the Delaware River.

Traci-Ann Delisser (Interview April 2006) – No personal update provided.

Robert G. Somers, MD (Interview March 2006) – Dr. Somers remained the chair of the Department of Surgery until January 2005 when he stepped down to continue the practice of breast surgery. Considering the aspects of his surgical career, he wants to be remembered most as a "caring" doctor and also a dedicated teacher.

Beth Cravitz Manusov (Interview March 2006) – Beth passed away suddenly in March 2007 from an illness unrelated to breast cancer. While seven months pregnant with her second child, Beth died of bacterial meningitis after complaining of an earache. A cesarean section was performed to save her baby's life. Up until her death, Beth continued her advocacy for early detection and raised money for breast cancer research. Beth is survived by her husband, Michael, their two daughters, her parents and sister. Her untimely death reminds us of her own advice, "You better appreciate your life because something can happen at any moment and you have to live for today."

Beth N. Peshkin, MS, CGC (Interview June 2007) – In 2006, she was appointed and still serves as the Education Director for the Jess and Mildred Fisher Center for Familial Cancer Research, an endowed center at Georgetown University, whose mission is to conduct state-of-the-art research on the prevention, treatment, and management of familial cancers in order to improve the medical and quality of life outcomes for women and men at risk for cancer.

Generosa Grana, MD (Interview October 2009) – Dr. Grana continues as director of the Cooper Cancer Institute and has a busy clinical practice. Her spare time is spent with her husband and three adolescent children. She still finds time to visit family in Spain where she enjoys the beautiful scenery, the great food and warm friendships.

James Grupenhoff (Interview April 2007) – No personal update provided.

Faye Feldman, CRNP, BC (Interview June 2007) – After being at the University of Maryland Greenebaum Cancer Center for five years and working with adults in a specialty setting, Faye decided to put her primary care training and Family Nurse Practitioner certificate to work in a retail based clinic. The career change has also allowed Faye to spend more time with her two young children. She is privileged to have been part of the lives of so many remarkable women and men, noting, "Cancer really teaches a person to treasure every second of ones' life." She hopes to one day return to working in the oncology field because no other part of her nursing career has been as personally and professionally rewarding.

Valerie & Michael Yasner (Interview March 2006) – Four years after this interview, Val is happy to say she is a 53 year old woman who knows the value of community. Her first expression of the strength that comes from community was through the founding of the breast cancer support group, Yad b" Yad, Hand in Hand. Since then, Val followed her passion in the area of nutrition and healthy eating. She now coordinates a Community Supported Agriculture program (CSA) that is in its second season. The CSA helps to support a local organic farmer who brings CSA members delicious weekly produce. By running weekly food demonstrations and cooking classes along with baking for a specialty shop, Val is able to share her love of cooking and healthy eating, and encourage a healthier community and planet. Val and Michael will celebrate their 29th wedding anniversary this year. Their children are confident young women pursuing their own dreams and ideals. They couldn't be prouder!

Steven Copit, MD (Interview October 2009) – Dr. Copit continues his practice at Jefferson Plastic Surgery. A devoted husband and father, he spends most of his free time with his wife and their two sons. His family enjoys skiing in the mountains of Utah and in other parts of the west.

Philla Barkhorn (Interview June 2008) – Philla, now 48 years old, is a four year breast cancer survivor. She continues her career as a portrait artist and has begun teaching art, both at the local senior center and the high school. Philla continues to be cancer free and is grateful for every day she can spend with her three children and husband.

Michele Rossi, LCSW (Interview March 2010) – Michele Rossi is currently working on a Ph.D. in Urban Affairs and Public Policy at the University of Delaware. After graduation (at age 52), she hopes to advocate for a wide range of social change, but most especially for greater civic engagement education for school children. She continues to run cancer support groups, sing in a rock and roll band and live with and care for her 84 year old father.

The Wellness Community Healing Garden
Springhouse Shrine of Peace, Laughter, and Memories

Like many 18th century houses, the house that now is home to The Wellness Community, in Wilmington, Delaware has a little building behind it that looks like a tiny house sunken into the ground. It's a springhouse—which was used to shelter a natural source for water, such as a spring or small creek, as well as a type of "refrigerator," as the water kept the small building cool all year round.

A tiny little house is fascinating to most people, but especially to children. The members of The Wellness Community support group for kids, Kids Circle/Teen Talk, were no exception. They got up the courage to check out the inside (in spite of spiders and dust) and then the building was all but forgotten. But then some sad things happened that changed the springhouse forever.

Kids Circle/Teen Talk is for kids experiencing the cancer of a loved one, often a parent. Two parents of children in the group died within a few weeks of each other. One of the children, a girl of about 10 who had been adopted from a Latin American country as a baby, reacted by doing what would have been natural in her home country. Without prompting, she constructed a shrine next to her bed of her Dad who just passed away, using items that belonged to him, along with photographs and a votive candle. Particularly touching was that she put his last deodorant there, which was scented, so she could "smell Dad" when she missed him.

The group talked about what she had done, and then what could be done as a group, to mark the occasion of a death. After some discussion, the idea of turning

the springhouse into a small "shrine" emerged. The kids in the group voted and chose the name, Springhouse Shrine of Peace, Laughter, and Memories. Funds were raised to renovate the little building.

When the building was dedicated, the ceremony that the children decided upon was used for the first time. Group members and their families and guests formed a semi-circle around the shrine's front door, while grieving children and their family members entered the shrine to light votive candles, and place items such as photos and other personal items of their deceased on a specially constructed shelf. Then, they sat on the provided bench and used their time in the shrine as they wanted. The members outside waited in silence, hands joined. When the grieving family emerged, they received hugs and condolences from the group. Per the children's rules, the items placed in the shrine had to be removed in a year, to mark that the grieving process was moving to a new stage.

Michele Rossi, LCSW
Kids Circle/Teen Talk
Group Facilitator
The Wellness Community

Acknowledgments

Publishing A Pink Ribbon Journey has been my passion and dream for the past five years. Writing the stories has been a true labor of love. I have been awestruck by the breast cancer survivors, their families, and the medical professionals. All of them eagerly and graciously, without hesitation or trepidation, shared their personal stories of hope and heartache, of perseverance and courage, so that my dream could become a reality. I owe a debt of gratitude to my photographer, Lesha Moore, and her husband, Eric for your unfailing commitment, patience, and flexibility these past five years. To our longtime family friend Louis Greenstein, a huge thank you. You were a valuable source of guidance and reference in the books early stages. Thank you to Evelyn Robles-Rodriguez, for your professional translation of the manuscript and website into Spanish, ensuring my commitment to reach the Hispanic communities served by Maria Matos and Generosa Grana. Thank you to my father, Alan Roth, and my three adoring sisters, Marsha, Sharon, and Debbie, and my other family and friends for your continued encouragement and support. A special hug of love and gratitude goes to my sister Sharon, you graciously offered your graphic artist skills and created this magnificent book we hold in our hands today. You brought to life my vision for a beautiful book which reflected the artistic integrity of Lesha's photographs. A special thank you to my friends, Judy Bleemer Baker, Lori Braunstein, Sean Hebbel and Rosalee Levine; all four of you connected me with several of the people profiled in this book. But most of all, from the bottom of my heart, I thank my loving and devoted partner, my husband, Joel Penn, for never giving up on me or my dream. Your endless words of encouragement rallied me to the end. To our three precious jewels, Shayna, Jeremy, and Marlena, thank you for your support and love. When I felt frustration or hopelessness, you three always offered words of support to keep me going. Shayna and Marlena, a heartfelt thank you for helping me select the many photographs accompanying the stories. I couldn't have made those difficult choices without your input and advice. And thank you to Jeremy, for offering up your computer tech skills, as manager of the bulletin board forum on my website www.pinkribbonjourney.com. I love you all very much!

Norma E. Roth

Glossary of Medical Terms

Bilateral mastectomy – the surgical removal of both breasts, usually for cancer

Biopsy – removal and examination, usually microscopic, of tissue from the living body, performed to establish precise diagnosis

BRCA1/2 – one of two genes (designated BRCA1 and BRCA2) that help repair damage to DNA, but when inherited in a defective state increase the risk of breast and ovarian cancer

Breast Reconstruction – a series of surgical procedures performed to recreate a breast using a woman's natural tissues

Chemotherapy – the treatment of cancer using specific chemical agents or drugs that are selectively destructive to malignant cells and tissues

DCIS (Ductal Carcinoma In Situ) – a cancer confined (that has not spread) to the mammary ducts

Fibroadenoma – a tumor composed of glandular (related to gland) and fibrous (containing fibers) tissues.

LCIS (Lobular Carcinoma In Situ) – a cancer confined (that has not spread) to the lobules or milk making glands.

Lumpectomy – surgical procedure removing a malignant tumor and a surrounding margin of normal breast tissue. Lymph nodes in the armpit (axilla) also may be removed. This procedure is called lymph node dissection

Lymphedema – blockage of the lymph vessels, with a resulting accumulation of lymphatic fluid in the interstitial tissues of the body

Lymph node – any of the small, oval or round bodies, located along the lymphatic vessels, that supply lymphocytes to the bloodstream and remove bacteria and foreign particles from the lymph.

Lymph node dissection – surgical removal of a group of lymph nodes

Mammogram – an x-ray film of the soft tissues of the breast produced by mammography

Mastectomy – excision of the breast

Metastasis – a secondary cancerous growth formed by transmission of cancerous cells from a primary growth located elsewhere in the body

Modified radical mastectomy – surgical removal of the entire breast and the lymphatic-bearing tissue in the armpit

MRI – the abbreviated term for magnetic resonance imaging. MRI uses a large circular magnet and radio waves to generate signals from atoms in the body. These signals are used to construct images of internal structures

Oncotype DX – a diagnostic test that quantifies the likelihood of disease recurrence in women with early-stage breast cancer and assesses the likely benefit from certain types of chemotherapy

Oophorectomy – surgical removal of the ovaries, usually for cancer

Peripheral neuropathy – a problem with the functioning of the nerves outside of the spinal cord. Symptoms may include numbness, tingling and weakness

Phyllodes tumor – a large, locally aggressive, sometimes metastatic fibroadenoma in the breast

Prophylactic – tending to ward off disease

Prosthesis – an artificial device used to replace a missing body part

Radiation therapy – sometimes called radiotherapy, x-ray therapy radiation treatment, cobalt therapy, electron beam therapy, or irradiation uses high energy, penetrating waves or particles such as x rays, gamma rays, proton rays, or neutron rays to destroy cancer cells or keep them from reproducing

Radical mastectomy – surgical removal of the entire breast, the pectoral muscles, the lymphatic-bearing tissue in the armpit, and other neighboring tissues

Support group – a group of people, sometimes led by a therapist, who provide each other moral support, information, and advice on problems relating to some shared characteristic or experience

Ultrasound – the use of ultrasonic waves for diagnostic or therapeutic purposes, specifically to visualize an internal body structure, monitor a developing fetus, or generate localized deep heat to the tissues

Unilateral mastectomy – surgical removal of one breast, usually for cancer

Breast Cancer Stages

Stage 0 – is very early breast cancer. The cancer cells are still only in the duct or lobule where they began.

Stage I – the tumor is small, 0 to 2 cm (about 1 inch) wide, with negative lymph nodes (no cancer cells in the lymph nodes). The tumor has not spread outside of the breast.

Stage II – the tumor is 2 to 5 cm (about 1 to 2 inches) wide, and lymph nodes under the arm on the same side of the body as the tumor may be positive (meaning that the lymph nodes have cancer cells in them) or the tumor is more than 5 cm (about 2 inches) wide, but the lymph nodes are still negative

Stage III, also known as locally advanced cancer, means one of the following: The tumor has grown larger than 5 cm wide, and cancer has spread to lymph nodes under the arm or, the tumor is any size, but more lymph nodes are now positive. These nodes may be under the arm and attached to one another or in the surrounding tissue and enlarged or, the tumor is any size and has spread to the chest wall or the skin or, the tumor is any size and there are positive lymph nodes in the chest above or just below the collar bone

Stage IV - the breast cancer is metastatic, it has spread to somewhere else in the body

Websites

www.cooperhealth.org/content/cancer/

http://fishercenter.georgetown.edu

www.thelatincenter.org

www.leshastudios.com

www.phillabarkhorn.com

www.pinkribbonjourney.com

www.sjra.com

www.wellnessdelaware.org

www.goodgriefcoaching.com

www.stothart.us/healingartisan

To purchase copies of this book and to join the journey, visit
www.pinkribbonjourney.com

This book is available in Spanish.
For information on how to purchase the Spanish version, visit our website.

Book signings and speaking engagements are handled by the author.
For inquiries email Norma@pinkribbonjourney.com

A percentage of the proceeds from this book will be donated to breast cancer charities.

Pink Ribbon Journey
Stories From the Heart

Celebrating Women with Breast Cancer

www.pinkribbonjourney.com